KUI

BOOK SYNOPSIS

Kunyaza is Africa's secret to female pleasure.

Originally from Rwanda, east-central Africa, the kunyaza sexual practice triggers female ejaculation and multiple orgasms in women during heterosexual encounters. The kunyaza technique is also practised in Uganda and Kenya, where it is known as kachabali.

Benefits of kunyaza include:
- facilitates female ejaculation and/or 'squirting,'
- triggers multiple orgasms in women,
- brings women to climax in less than five minutes,
- helps men last longer in the bedroom,
- enhances female pleasure,
- stimulation of the K-Spot, and
- an effective treatment for female orgasmic disorder.

Kunyaza examines the cultural impact of Rwanda's pleasure-based sensual tradition and investigates whether it empowers women.

The book also explores the psychology of female desire, analyses female ejaculation and G-Spot studies, and investigates the controversial practice of labia pulling.

Drawing on extensive research from Western-trained sexologists, psychologists, and ssengas (female sex educators) from Africa, the book provides an intimate and illustrated guide on how to make a woman ejaculate.

ABOUT THE AUTHOR

Habeeb Akande is a British-born writer and historian of Nigerian descent. He is the author of five published books on race, erotic Arabic literature, Islam and Brazil, including; *Illuminating the Darkness: Blacks and North Africans in Islam, A Taste of Honey: Sexuality and Erotology in Islam,* and *Illuminating the Blackness: Blacks and African Muslims in Brazil.*

Elegance is not about being noticed, it's about being remembered.

HABEEB AKANDE

KUNYAZA

THE SECRET TO
FEMALE PLEASURE

RABAAH
PUBLISHERS

First Published in England by Rabaah Publishers
7 Granary Square
Epping Place
London, N1 1FA
www.rabaah.com

Written by: Habeeb Akande

A catalogue record of this book is available from the British Library

ISBN-13: 978-0-9574845-6-6

Cover illustration: *Take The Leap* by Everitte Barbee. The figure of a woman jumping is created using the Arabic Diwani Djali script. The text reads "Always do what you are afraid to do" and is repeated three times to create the shape of a woman conquering her fear. Reproduced by permission of the artist.

Illustration sources:
Page 30: Map of East African countries. (Credit: The Rwandan).
Page 69: The external female genitalia. (Credit: Anatomy & Physiology Openstax website).
Page 71: Clitoris anatomy (Credit: Amphis).
Page 96: Fluids released during sexual activities table. (Credit: Zlatko Pastor).
Page 111: Vulva. (Credit: Unknown).
Page 111: Approximate location of the G-Spot. (Credit: iflscience.com).
Page 112: Horizonal and zigzagging stimulation of the vulva. (Credit: Juan Pablo Gomez).
Page 114: Man performing kunyaza on woman laying down. (Credit: Igituba.org).

Printed and bound by:
CPI Group (UK) Ltd, Croydon, CR0 4YY

"A river that forgets its source will surely dry up." – Yoruba proverb

Contents

Introduction: The Future is Female Ejaculation

"God gave that ocean to all of us." – Mama Cuysa from Gitega, Burundi

In most of the world's cultures, sexual pleasure for women is not considered important, whereas in Rwanda, East Africa, it is regarded as a "basic right." Rwanda's culture of female ejaculation is in stark contrast to most Western attitudes towards female sexuality. Historically in the West female pleasure has been shrouded in mystery. In particular, female ejaculation has been a matter of controversy for centuries. Many sex researchers deny its existence and others state that the large erotic expulsions ('squirting') is urine and not actual female ejaculate. This is despite the fact that many women report that the erotic experience of involuntary fluid emission during orgasm is different from the voluntary expulsion of urine. Unlike in Rwanda, female ejaculation remains a subject of much debate in Western societies (the United States, Canada, the UK, and Western Europe). It's largely a cultural issue.

Sexuality is culturally determined and defined. The values that are attached to sex and sexual behaviour varies across cultures. For instance, the sexual practices and attitudes of black women in Rwanda, East Africa are not necessarily the same as the sexual practices and attitudes of white women in Western Europe. Since Europe's colonisation of Africa and the exposure to Western values, many African people have adopted a "Westernised" approach to sex and sexuality. Whilst this has proved beneficial in some senses, others have decried that the "white man's" cultural imperialism will result in the loss of Rwandan cultural practices, namely the sexual practices of *gukuna* and *kunyaza,* which reportedly enhance female pleasure and cause female ejaculation respectively.

Prior to Europe's colonisation of Africa, many African countries had a positive attitude towards female pleasure and female sexuality. In Rwanda the female orgasm is celebrated, and the female ejaculate is considered sacred. Traditional Rwandan culture not only acknowledged female ejaculation but developed a sexual practice triggering the large expulsion of fluid, commonly known as 'squirting,' during heterosexual encounters. The female-orientated sexual practice called kunyaza is derived from the word '*kunyara*,' meaning 'to urinate.' Another practice called gukuna involving the stretching of the labia was commonly practised amongst girls and women prior to marriage. It is believed that labia pulling helps women ejaculate.

Both practices began with a woman, was passed down by women and is largely preserved by women. Under the tutelage of *ssengas* (paternal aunts) who serve as female sex educators, African women would speak openly and honestly about intimate matters in women-only spaces away from the male gaze. There was no shame in a woman expressing desire and female sexual agency was not taboo in pre-modern Rwanda. African attitudes towards female sexuality soon changed when European Christians colonised Rwanda. The prudish attitude of Europeans influenced many Africans as the sexual traditions started to decrease amongst Western-educated Rwandans.

Traditionalists fear that Rwanda is in danger of losing their cultural traditions, especially kunyaza, due to Western cultural imperialism and Christian missionaries. Ali Kakonge Simba, 37, a sex herbalist and kunyaza teacher, explains,

> It goes back to colonial times. In order to control us, the white people brought new ideas and new systems to Africans to derail our culture...some practices were actually discarded because the missionaries thought they were dirty, that it was a sin to the Christian God to keep practising kunyaza, all because the white men didn't know about it. [1]

To combat this, a growing number of sex researchers, both inside and outside of Africa, are taking it upon themselves to preserving kunyaza, Rwanda's age-old pleasure tradition facilitating female ejaculation. For many Rwandans, female ejaculation is the past, present and future. A strong advocate for reviving Rwanda's ancient sexual traditions, Vestine Dusabe is a sex educator and radio host with a mission; promoting sexual pleasure and Rwanda's culture of female ejaculation. "We talk because we do not want our culture to disappear," Dusabe says,

> We found that there is a lack of knowledge about sex among Rwandese people. They don't know how to do sex at all. Men come

---

[1] McCool, A., 'The joy of kunyaza: women's pleasure comes first in Rwanda'

from a bar or work and just want to have sex without talking or romancing their wife.

We tell the men that you're not supposed to just open the door and go inside, you have first to knock, when they say come in, then you can go in. We teach the men where and how to touch a woman.

We talk about how a woman is supposed to treat her husband, we talk about hygiene between couples.

Rwanda's Secret to Female Pleasure

In the small east-central African country of Rwanda, women's pleasure comes first. Female orgasm is a regular occurrence in many African bedrooms due to the ancient sexual technique. Originally from Rwanda, the kunyaza foreplay technique has the reputation of triggering female ejaculation and multiple orgasms in women during consensual heterosexual encounters.[2] In Uganda and Kenya, the sexual practice of kunyaza is known as kachabali.

In contrast to Western societies, where the female orgasm is elusive when a man is involved, the opposite is the case in Africa. Studies have reported that East African women are more likely to experience orgasm and ejaculation with their male partner than Western women. This is primarily due to different cultural practices and attitudes towards female sexuality. According to Rwandan sexologist and kunyaza educator, Vestine Dusabe, 80% to 90% of Rwandan women are capable of ejaculation. In contrast, 10% to 54% of Western women experience the large expulsion of ejaculatory fluid during orgasm, according to a study reported in *The Journal of Sexual Medicine*.[3]

Several scientific studies analysing the biochemical composition of the female ejaculate conclude that squirting is actually urine. Many women reject these academic findings and believe that squirting is indeed a reality. In Rwanda, female ejaculators are extolled as is their ability to emit large gushes of liquid during sexual play with their spouses. There is no doubt amongst Rwandan sex educators that female ejaculation is not urine, as American sex educator Lux Alptraum concurs,

regardless of the biological basis of female ejaculation, the physical experience is, at its heart, a pure expression of female sexual

---

[2] Bizimana, N., 'Another way for lovemaking in Africa: Kunyaza, a traditional sexual technique for triggering female orgasm at heterosexual encounters.'

[3] Pastor, Z, 'Female Ejaculation Orgasm vs Coital Incontinence: A Systematic Review.'

pleasure. Insisting that female ejaculation is really just confused urination doesn't just denigrate women's ability to understand our own bodies – it also positions female sexual pleasure as filthy, dirty, and ultimately less than the celebrated male orgasm.

Culturally men are expected to bring their women to climax and 'produce the water' as explained by a Rwandan woman in the 2016 *Sacred Water* documentary about the kunyaza practice;

If, when making love, a man doesn't let the water spring, he will be frustrated, and the woman offended. It's cultural. All women have the ability (to ejaculate).

Since the kunyaza pleasure-orientated female-friendly technique was discovered over 150 years ago, it has evolved to encompass other practices to enhance women's pleasure and ability to ejaculate. Today, the kunyaza tradition, taught primarily by female sex educators, known as ssengas, includes teaching the psychology of female desire, sexual health, mental foreplay, *gukuna* (labia pulling), sex positions and encouraging open communication between lovers to increase the woman's ability to expel a flood of sensual 'water' during kunyaza/kachabali. Research by German-based Rwandan sex researcher, Dr. Nsekuye Bizimana, found that the kunyaza technique is an effective treatment for female orgasmic disorder,[4] and it can induce orgasm in less than five minutes for some women.

The kunyaza technique consists of a man using his erect penis to stimulate a woman's vulva to increase arousal and ability to squirt before, or during climax. Non-penetrative stimulation of the labia minora and clitoris with the glans penis includes stroking, tapping and rubbing of the vulva to tease and heighten pleasure prior to penetration.

The man then proceeds to penetrative stimulation by way of rhythmically performing deep and / or shallow thrusts inside the vagina once the woman is fully lubricated to prepare her for an intense orgasm. Focusing on clitoral stimulation, kunyaza sex includes vulval stimulation and vaginal penetration. Alternatively, the woman can use the man's penis to practice kunyaza on

[4] Bizimana, N., Kunyaza: An African Contribution to the Treatment of Female Orgasmic Dysfunction, 20th World Congress for Sexual Health 2011

herself to enable a truly loving squirting orgasm. Despite its reported effectiveness, the kunyaza tradition is not well known outside of Africa.

Things are changing. The Internet has become a source of sexual knowledge and pleasure for many of the world's population. Sexual content is easily assessible on the Internet. Young men in rural villages in Rwanda can easily access pornography over the Internet, where sex is depicted in ways that conflict with the traditional values imparted by their parents. Nowadays, online Western pornography is where many Africans learn about sex, according to Jean, a 26-year-old from Rwanda;

> In the middle classes no one has time for that. Dad's working, mum's working, so you've just got TV and the internet. We're self-taught, basing sex mostly on what we see in Western porn, and you don't see much kunyaza there.

That being said, there is a growing attempt to preserve this traditional African sexual practice from people inside and outside the continent. To my knowledge, *Kunyaza: The Secret to Female Pleasure*, is the first book about the East African sex technique in the English language. This book explores the cultural impact of the technique and investigates whether the kunyaza tradition is empowering for heterosexual women, particularly in East Africa. The book also investigates whether kunyaza enhances sexual pleasure for women, the mysteries of female ejaculation and the controversial practice of labia pulling in East and Central Africa. The book aims to raise awareness of the contribution of Africans to female sexuality by examining the effectiveness of kunyaza to induce female ejaculation and multiple orgasms in women.

Drawing on extensive research from African-based sexologists, sexual health educators, psychologists, and ssengas (female sex educators), the book provides an intimate guide to this traditional African sensual practice which has the reputation of triggering female ejaculation.'

Africa's Pleasure-Based Sex Education
Pleasure-based sex education is not uncommon in Africa. In traditional African cultures, a holistic pleasure-focused approach to sex education is adopted to teach people about sexual pleasure, sexual ethics, consent,

biology, sexual health, and the physiology of sex. Female sex educators in Africa make use of a number of traditional practices and techniques to prepare a bride for marriage and ensure social stability by keeping couples happily married. Handed down the generations by women for women, traditional sex and beauty practices include; *kayan mata* (herbal aphrodisiac) in Nigeria, *dukhan* (womb steaming)[5] in Sudan, *jigida* (waistbeads) in West Africa, *gukuna* (labia pulling) and *kunyaza* (female ejaculation inducement) in Rwanda.

In northern Nigeria, a five-century-old herbal aphrodisiac tradition aimed at enhancing female sensuality is growing in popularity in southwest Nigeria. Known as *kayan mata* ('women's property') in the Hausa language, it refers to a range of herbs, spices and home-made concoctions to keep the spark alive and increase desire. Sellers of herbal aphrodisiacs in Nigeria are usually women who also provide advice on how women can have a healthy and enjoyable love live. *Zuman mata*, which translates as 'women's honey' is guaranteed to "keep a man coming back." The popular honey-based aphrodisiac is to be applied on the vulva or inside the vagina to facilitate lubrication. Other *kayan mata* practices are said to tighten the vaginal walls and muscles in addition to increasing pleasure. In conservative Nigeria, pleasure is a woman's God-given right which Nigerian Muslim females are taught to prepare them for marriage. For some, sex without *kayan mata* is like cooking without salt!

In contrast to Africa, the Western model of sex education has often been described as inadequate and outdated.[6] Sex education in the West tends to only focus on biology, sexual health and the physiology of sex. There is very little discussion on consent, sexual ethics and pleasure, especially female pleasure. The clitoris, female orgasm and female ejaculation are shrouded in mystery in the West. In fact, women's sexual desire was not even recognised by Western intellectuals until the 1960s. Christian Victorian morality governed sexual attitudes throughout much of the Western world and British

---

[5] The *dukhan* practice tightens a woman's vagina and drives her husband wild according to traditional Sudanese culture.

[6] Sex education in the West needs to focus on pleasure according to sexual and relationship (SRE) professionals. Alex Phillips, SRE policy lead at Terrence Higgins Trust, UK's leading sexual health charity, said, "Our research shows that nine out of ten (89%) young people are not taught about sex in relation to pleasure – instead, what's being taught is usually focused on the biological basics, how to avoid pregnancies and so on. 'It is so important that young people hear the message that sex is supposed to be pleasurable and consensual."

colonies, where 'good women' were taught to be prudish.[7] Not much has changed nowadays as many European and American cultures have held on to Victorian attitudes about sex being 'dirty' and 'shameful.' This unhealthy attitude to sex and female sexuality resulted in sex being viewed as an act mainly for procreation and not pleasure. When pleasurable sex is not taught, unsatisfying sex becomes the norm.

Unsurprisingly many women have accepted unsatisfying sex thinking that is a normal part of a relationship. Their male partners do not make the effort to satisfy them as they think women's pleasure is not important. Pornography has also played a part in many phallocentric Western societies.[8] Pornography has become a primary source of sex education, and has a harmful effect on the sexual behaviours and attitudes of young adults, research reveals.[9] According to a UK study, 60% of young people watch porn to learn about sex despite the fact that almost 75% admitted that it gave unrealistic expectations.[10] A 2018 report found that one in five young people in Ireland think pornography is a "useful" source of information about healthy sexual relationships.[11]

Research in the United States have also found the growing epidemic of online pornography amongst American adolescents. Multiple studies have found that porn is negatively shaping people's ideas about pleasure, intimacy and relationships. The pervasive influence of pornography gives people false ideas about sexual pleasure. Women in porn are often depicted as the object of the man's pleasure which has led to a dismissive attitude of the woman's pleasure. Such problematic attitudes are also reflected in mainstream media across many cultures around the world which portray unrealistic notions of female sexuality.

---

[7] Victorian morality describes a set of values that espouse prudery, sexual restraint, and a strict social conduct.

[8] Pornography is defined in the Oxford dictionary as, "printed or visual material containing the explicit description or display of sexual organs or activity, intended to stimulate sexual excitement."

[9] Sun, C., Bridges, *et al.*, 'Pornography and the Male Sexual Script: An Analysis Consumption and Sexual Relations,' pp. 983-994

[10] The study was carried out by the National Union of Students (NUS) in November 2014, involving 2,502 students in the UK.

[11] Commissioned by Youth Work Ireland (YWI), the largest youth organisation in Ireland, The Positive Sexual Relations Report took the opinions of 1,056 respondents aged between 14 and 24 years of age in March and April 2018. The report examined the opinions and attitudes of young people in Ireland towards healthy sexual relationships, consent and inappropriate sexual behaviour.

Fortunately, there are cultures which acknowledge and celebrate women's sexuality and right to pleasure. Surprisingly to many, in medieval Arab and North African Muslim cultures sex and female sexual pleasure were openly talked about and considered part of a fulfilling marital life. Muslim intellectuals wrote comprehensive books on the physical and spiritual delights of sex for both men and women. In a number of East African cultures, female sensuality is sacred, and men are expected to satisfy their wives using the age-old kunyaza technique.

Sexually Dissatisfied Women

Study after study shows that sexual pleasure, self-esteem and satisfaction have a profound impact on our physical and mental wellbeing. It is a natural and vital part of our health and happiness. Oftentimes, in Western societies, this premise is accepted fairly easily when it comes to men. Men feel entitled to pleasure and be pleasured. Women, on the other hand, appear mostly as sexual objects rather than as subjects. Female sexual pleasure is poorly understood across most societies. There is little scientific research on the topic and even sex researchers tend to shy away from discussing it.

According to a study in the *Journal of Sexual Medicine*, less than 30% of gynaecologists routinely ask their patients about pleasure and sexual satisfaction. Most women require at least twenty minutes of clitoral stimulation to achieve orgasm and 70% of women do not orgasm regularly during sexual encounters. During orgasm, 10% to 54% of women experience the involuntary emission of fluid during orgasm ranging from 30 to 150ml. Several studies show that most women do not frequently experience orgasm, and less than 30% of women have difficulties experiencing an orgasm. A comprehensive review study analysing 33 studies over 80 years found that 80% of women have difficulty reaching climax from vaginal intercourse.[12] Other studies have shown that up to 15% of women have never experienced an orgasm despite being sexually active for many years. A 2018 UK study found that almost half of women are dissatisfied with their sex lives. The report by Public Health England (PHE) revealed that women aged 25 to 34 were the least satisfied in bed, with 49% complaining they lacked sexual enjoyment.

---

[12] The study was reported in *The Case of The Female Orgasm* by Elisabeth Lloyd.

Based on a poll of 7,367 women aged 16 to 64, 42% of the women said they were unhappy with their sex lives. Dr Jane Dickson, Vice President of the Faculty of Sexual and Reproductive Healthcare, said:

> The importance of having a healthy, enjoyable sexual life cannot be overstated as this strongly contributes to general wellbeing. However, there is still much stigma and embarrassment when it comes to sexual function – especially when we are talking about women's sexual pleasure. Society still relegates women's sexual pleasure to the background.

Female Orgasm and Culture

Views of the female orgasm differ among cultures, which is not surprising. Given the vast diversity of values, attitudes, and practices among the world's many cultures, it is natural that sexual behaviour is not exempt from cultural interpretations. Yet, historical texts from a variety of cultures eloquently describe pleasurable orgasmic sensations resulting from sexual activity.

In most of the world's cultures, discussions concerning how men and women can and should experience sexual pleasure, including orgasm, have been a part of their tradition. Sometimes these discussions are intended to reduce sexual activity. At other times, discussions are intended to foster a better marriage – for example, in some Islamic cultures, men are encouraged to withhold ejaculation until they are certain that their wife is satisfied.

Each of us are embedded within a culture and influenced by it. We are products of our environment. Our view of the female orgasm and the prevailing view in our culture may be aligned or may be in conflict. In this time of growing cross-cultural relationships, sex researchers suggest that, for the sake of more fulfilling sexual relationships, people should learn as much as possible about their own culture and their partner's culture if it is different from their own. In this way, each person probably has the best chance of maximising his or her sexual experiences.[13]

As previously mentioned, in contemporary Western cultures, female ejaculation and women's orgasms are considered mythical. However, in some East African cultures, the female orgasm is venerated. So much so that

---

[13] Komisaruk B., *et al.*, *The Orgasm Answer Guide*, pp. 113-114

men who aren't able to bring their wives to climax are ridiculed! This is a result of cultural traditions and societal expectations of male-female relationships. Men are expected to sexually please women. According to prominent Rwandan sexologist, Vestine Dusabe, the kunyaza tradition consists of a man psychologically and physically satisfying his wife. Dusabe travels to several countries teaching women about the 'sacred water' of female ejaculation to ensure that Rwanda's sexual traditions (kunyaza and gukuna) are preserved. Gukuna, referring to labia pulling, is said to increase a woman's ability to ejaculate during kunyaza. It is a controversial practice in many Western countries, as some consider labia pulling to be a form of female genital mutilation (FGM), though many Africans disagree.

The German-based Rwandan sex researcher, Dr. Bizimana authored two books in French and German about kunyaza, *Le Secret de l'amour à l'Africaine* (The Secret to African Love) in 2008 and *Kunyaza: Multiple Orgasmen und Weibliche Ejakulation mit Afrikanischer Liebeskunst* (Kunyaza: Multiple Orgasms and Female Ejaculation with African Lovemaking) in 2009. Bizimana also carried out some research on the effectiveness of the kunyaza technique for women suffering from orgasmic dysfunction, which he presented to sexual health professionals at the World Congress for Sexual Health (WAS) conference in 2011.

Although no longer widely practised in Rwanda, the kunyaza technique gained international attention after the release of the award-winning documentary film, *Sacred Water* (2016), and online articles about the technique on prominent websites across the world such as; Cosmopolitan Brazil, Cosmopolitan Germany, American based online magazine Ozy, the UK's New Internationalist, Cosmopolitan UK, AskMen, and South Africa's News24. The *Sacred Water* film explored the kunyaza tradition and the particularities of Rwandan sexual culture.

Britain's 'Medical Machismo' Culture

Some of the controversy surrounding female sexuality revolves around a reluctance to accept the testimonies of women who say they can ejaculate as credible evidence. The on-going debate of whether the female ejaculate or its source, the female prostate (G-Spot), exists has been investigated in dozens of studies. The real question is not whether female ejaculation exists, it is why many researchers do not believe the testimonies of female ejaculators. The

17

scepticism by Western academics about women's ability to report accurately on their sexual responses is a form of controlling female sexuality.

Cultural attitudes influence female sexuality studies. An example of this can be found with the aftermath of a 2010 British study on the existence of the G-Spot. The researchers concluded that the G-Spot does not exist even though 56% of women reported its existence. Following the study's publication, a month later French gynaecologist Odile Buisson said the study was a demonstration of a cultural difference in attitudes to sex. Dismissing the study's findings, Buisson said the scientists had fallen victim to an Anglo-Saxon tendency to reduce the mysteries of female sexuality to absolutes. Describing researchers who deny the existence of the G-Spot as a type of 'medical machismo,' Buisson adds,

> I don't want to stigmatise at all but I think the Protestant, liberal, Anglo-Saxon character means you are very pragmatic. There has to be a cause for everything, a gene for everything. It's totalitarian.

The researchers' attempt to set clear parameters on something variable and ambiguous such as female sexuality was characteristic of British scientific attitudes to sex, Buisson said.

Since the prudery of the Victorian era between the nineteen and twentieth century, modern day white Anglo-Saxon (British) culture have followed suit. Acclaimed British author of *The Joy of Sex*, Alex Comfort (d. 2000), claimed that white people's social awkwardness and uptight culture was the reason why many of them did not excel in the art of lovemaking, unlike black people. Learning to relax and be more carefree will help improve white people's perceived 'inherent' anxiousness, Comfort says;

> Where black people of both sexes undoubtedly do score sexually is that Black culture has never lost its body sense as White [people] has and isn't physically uptight. Its body language is much freer and accordingly many black people are better at sex than anxious Wasps [White Anglo-Saxon Protestant] [14] for the same reason that they dance much better. Some degree of soul, rhythm, and body sense is something we others [i.e. white people] need to relearn. [15]

---

[14] Wasp is an abbreviation for White Anglo-Saxon Protestant. The term refers to white people originally from northern Europe.
[15] Comfort, A., 'More Joy of Sex vol. 2,', in Comfort, A., 1987, *The Complete Joy of Sex*, p. 91

Pioneer of female sexuality studies and American sex researcher Beverly Whipple believes Anglo-Saxon and Western culture has a lot it can learn from other cultures which have a more positive attitude towards the female orgasm. In her best-selling book, *The G-Spot and Other Discoveries about Human Sexuality* (1982), Whipple said;

> Knowledge of sexuality and sexual techniques is more cultural than instinctive. Cultures less sexually repressive than our own [Western culture] celebrate the existence of female orgasm and teach their members methods of achieving it. In such cultures female orgasm is the expected state of affairs.[16]

In search of a more free and expressive culture, nowadays many white (Anglo-Saxons) people travel to Africa to learn about female sexuality and pleasure. The notion that Western cultures are 'sexually liberated' and the most progressive, has been challenged by many Westerners who have visited Rwanda and were made aware of the East African country's gender politics and female-centred sexual traditions. In a field study carried out in Rwanda, interviewed male respondents joked about how '*mzungu*' women (white/European women) never leave Rwanda once they have experienced kunyaza, thereby implying the superior pleasure possible with this Rwandan cultural practice.[17]

Rwandan Culture

Since the 1994 genocide, Rwanda has become a leading advocate for gender equality.[18] In the World Economic Forum's 2017 Global Gender Gap Report,[19] Rwanda is ranked fourth out of 144 countries, ahead of the UK (15) and the United States (49). Half of Rwanda's supreme court judges are women, and the country's parliament is 61% female, the highest proportion in the world. Recently, the country has also made great strides to address gender-based violence (GBV) and women's right to sexual pleasure, through

---

[16] Ladas, A., *The G-Spot: And Other Discoveries About Human Sexuality*, p. 41

[17] Bjarke, O., 'Let's Talk About Sex: Comparing Notes from Qualitative Research on Men, Relationships and Sex in South Africa and Rwanda.', p. 103

[18] The 1994 Rwandan genocide, in which the majority killed were men, encouraged President Paul Kagame to put women's empowerment at the forefront of government policy. An estimated 800,000 people were massacred when Rwanda's Hutu majority ethnic group turned against the Tutsi minority ethnic group. Approximately 21,000 people were killed in two days.

[19] The Global Gender Gap Report benchmarks 144 countries on their progress towards gender parity across four thematic dimensions: Economic Participation and Opportunity, Educational Attainment, Health and Survival, and Political Empowerment.

the works of women right's activists and anthropologists. In truth, Western culture has a lot it can learn about female sexuality and gender equality from traditional Rwandan culture, a Western journalist said;

> Where the Western world likes to pretend to be an advocate of sexual liberation for women, it comes to show that we still have a great deal to learn, and the candour and sincerity of Rwandan culture concerning female sexuality can serve as a grand example.

In a light-hearted discussion about 'Western people's ignorance' of female ejaculation, sexologist Vestine Dusabe, said during her popular radio programme *Zirara Zubakwa* on relationship counselling and sex education in Rwanda;

> Does that water really exist?
> White people don't believe in it because they don't know it.
> They have never tried to let that water spring.

According to Mama Cuysa from Gitega, Burundi in central Africa, most women are capable of ejaculation, "God gave that ocean to all of us. It was created for our husbands' pleasure and peace." Former lawyer and best-selling American sex writer, Gabrielle Moore, of the 'Squirting Orgasms Shortcuts' video series, said the following after finding out about kunyaza from Bizimana's book;

> Since I'm always eager to find out new things and experience as much as I can sexually, I went ahead and bought the book for my husband and we studied it together. After trying the tricks they taught us, I must go ahead and confess: it was like nothing I have tried before! I experienced the fastest and most powerful couple of orgasms in my life! And it's not hard to do either, so what are YOU waiting for? This (kunyaza) is a nice substitute for oral sex, if your girlfriend is one of those women that don't really feel comfortable with it...I want other women to experience the joy and happiness I felt.

An East African Tradition of Squirting

Euphemistically referred to as 'pouring rivers,' 'waterfalls,' 'water' and 'the ocean,' the expulsion of large quantities of fluid from a woman's urethra is a venerated tradition in East African cultures. Rwandan women in particular are known for their ability to ejaculate due to the kunyaza technique. Men who are not able to help their wives experience the 'joyful water' should be blamed according to Rwandan sex therapist Vestine Dusabe,

> Your husbands can't satisfy you. It's a real problem when a man doesn't do kunyaza to his wife...When a man doesn't make love to his wife properly, he will say she is dry, even if she has plenty of water.

In western Uganda, a woman's ability to expel fluid during sexual stimulation is part of womanhood. Ugandan academic and sex researcher Sylvia Tamale reported that an African sexuality teacher informed her;

> I myself was truly ignorant about female ejaculation until I met my current lover. If your lover knows what he is doing, you'll pour rivers and experience multiple orgasms at the same time.

The 'secret to squirting' craze has also spread to Kenya by way of Uganda. Known as *kachabali* in Uganda and Kenya, kunyaza is "the greatest Ugandan export to Kenya" according to Kenyan sex writer Valentine Njoroge. In a Kenyan lifestyle website, a woman revealed that she was introduced to kachabali at the age of twenty by a female friend when she was at university. "She initiated me into this form of orgasm, which is similar to urinating. She said it's mind-blowing. I however never experienced it until when I was 28. I guess men are just not patient enough with us." According to Kenyan sex and relationship therapist Maurice Matheka, squirting has become a marvel among Kenyan couples because people are becoming more open with their sexuality. He says,

> Our sexual behaviour has been a bit reserved because of the way we were brought up. Sex was more of an act of procreation rather than pleasure.

The ability to make a woman squirt is expected and desired amongst East African men, Dennis Muganwa, an event organiser in Kenya and Uganda explains,

> It is an untaught sex rule. Some men in the western part of Uganda and Rwanda will in fact not date a lady if she can't kunyara (ejaculate). As a matter of fact, mattresses in these countries, especially those in hotels, have liners to shield the foam from the generous amount of 'water spillage' that the women squish out.

Lawyer and founder of the online sex toy shop, *G-Spot Kenya*, Beverly Munga, claims that most Kenyan men are not attentive to women's needs once they have attained climax. After moving back to Kenya from the UK, Munga launched her sex toy business in which she is trying to demystify the belief that squirting is a preserve of Ugandan and Rwandese women only.

Amplifying African Women's Voices

Although the kunyaza practice is a mutually pleasurable act, its primary focus is female pleasure. The ability to make a woman ejaculate is a central feature of Rwandan masculinity. The man who is not equipped to do this, it not considered to be a good husband. Women have a God-given right to be pleasured and a man is expected to fulfil his role as a husband by satisfying his wife's physical needs and 'produce the water.' The Rwandan tradition of men satisfying women, in and outside of the bedroom, is at odds with Western culture in which sex tends to be centered on the pleasure of a man and female ejaculation is taboo. This is not the case in Rwanda and parts of East Africa where the kunyaza tradition is still practised. Traditionally, the teachings of kunyaza was passed down orally by women to other women. These female teachers often taught in forests and villages away from male interference.

Nowadays, African women's perspectives are not always heard in Western studies about female sexuality in Africa, unless they are speaking about FGM, sexual assault or sexually transmitted infections (STIs). The male or white female perspective is often centered in such studies which is problematic. African women are more than capable of speaking for themselves and controlling their own narrative. As one female sex educator from Eritrea, Sara, informed me, "We African women do not need white women to tell us how to look after our men!" She went on to explain why she felt the African woman's perspective on female sexuality is often marginalised in female sexuality studies. Sara adds,

> We have our own traditions, culture and religions in Africa. The frustration many African women have is white people imposing their Christian religion and feminism ideology on us. We do not need white women or Western-educated Africans telling us how we should think and behave as women and wives.

Women's Rights and Feminism

Feminism is defined as "the advocacy of women's rights on the ground of the equality of the sexes." Many feminists would like to 'dismantle the patriarchy' where men are in positions of power. Feminism is also defined as "the belief in the social, economic political and ideological quality of the sexes." Although largely originating in the West, feminism is manifested worldwide and is represented by various institutions committed to activity on behalf of women's rights and interest.

Whilst the advocacy of women's rights in the Western world is commonly referred to as part of the feminist movement, some women oppose it. Many women in non-Western countries, or those that believe in traditional gender roles reject the feminism ideology due to cultural and religious views. Sometimes referred to as 'white feminism,' the feminism movement is categorised into 'three waves' or 'four waves.'

The issue of women's rights in the West first became prominent during the French and American revolutions in the late 18th century. In Britain it was not until the emergence of the suffragette movement in the late 19th century that there was significant political change. This period, 1830s to early 1900s, is known as the first-wave of feminism which focused on fighting for equal contract and property rights for women.

A second-wave of feminism arose in the 1960s, with an emphasis on the workplace, sexuality, family and reproductive rights for women. A third-wave was identified in the late 1980s and 1990s, as a reaction against the perceived lack of focus on class and race issues in the first and second waves. The third-wave of feminism (1990s to the 2010s) saw the emergence of new feminist currents and theories such as intersectionality, womanism (within black feminism), sex positivity, transfeminism and postmodern feminism. Some feminists argue that a fourth-wave of feminism began around 2012 and is associated with the use of social media. The fourth-wave focuses on seeking justice for women and fighting against sexual harassment and violence against women.

Whilst many feminists claim that anyone who fights for women's rights should be identified as a 'feminist,' some oppose the feminism ideology as Muslim writer and women's rights activist Zara Faris explains, "The matter of women's rights has never been the exclusive preserve of feminists, so questioning feminism and its methods, as this discussion will do, is not tantamount to questioning the need to safeguard women's rights as defined by an ideology other than feminism." Other white feminism critics such as black American activist, Rachel Elizabeth Cargle, have described liberal white women's feminism as "toxic" and "white supremacy in heels."

In Africa, many women consider feminism to be a "white woman issue" and reject Western feminists claim to fight for African women's rights. Based on their cultural traditions and religious beliefs, women in Africa, express concern with the 'colonial mindset' of Western-educated peoples thinking that their concept of womanhood is more advanced than those in 'less-developed' countries. There are also growing numbers of educated African women who self-identify as feminists but do not agree with 'white feminism.' For these feminists, or 'womanists,' their approach is one which is Afro-centric and should preserve African cultural traditions providing that they are beneficial to women. Some Westerners describe African sexual traditions like kunyaza as an emancipatory feminist practice, others argue that it isn't as "it can sit comfortably with male control over the woman's body," freelance journalist Alice McCool writes.

Feminism remains a topical debate amongst non-white peoples, particularly in Africa amongst women's rights activist and sex educators. When I asked an experienced Rwandan-based sex educator whether kunyaza is compatible with feminism, she replied;

> Feminists do not speak for women here. We have our own culture and traditions. We do not need white people to save us! Westerners should respect our kunyaza tradition or leave us alone.

Brazil's Celebration of Female Orgasm and Kunyaza

When one thinks of Brazil, images of scantily clad women strolling along the beach or beautiful women dancing Samba during Carnival may arise. But away from travel brochure images and into Brazilian culture, one finds a traditional and sexually conservative society. The traditional view that female sexuality is less important than male sexuality is widely accepted among men and women of different educational and ethnic backgrounds in South America's most populous country. In an attempt to change attitudes, a Brazilian councilman dedicated a day to educate people about the importance of female pleasure in a relationship. Known as International Female Orgasm Day, the 8 August is a non-official holiday seeking to raise awareness about female sexuality and women's right to sexual pleasure. Councillor Arimateo Dantas dedicated the day to the female orgasm as compensation to the "sexual debt" he owed his wife.

Now celebrated in a number of countries around the world, the Day encourages women to learn more about their bodies, desire and sexuality. According to sex researcher Jacqueline Brendler, loss of sexual desire is commonly experienced by Brazilian women where traditional gender roles are still expected to be observed in the country's "machismo culture." Some studies report 28% of Brazilian women find it difficult to achieve climax, a national study reported that only 20% of women responded that sex is "a source of pleasure and satisfaction."[20] Several Brazilian articles report the kunyaza technique as an effective method to induce orgasm.

Ironically it was on 8 August 2015, that I was first made aware of Rwanda's sexual practice. Few months after the release of my book *Illuminating the Performance*, on erotic African literature, I received an email from a reader asking why I didn't mention the African technique in my book. At the time I was not aware of kunyaza and began to investigate this mysterious African technique which had the reputation of facilitating female ejaculation.

As I read about the tapping and rubbing of the clitoris with the penis head, I noticed the similarity of the Rwandan sexual practice with an ancient Arab sexual practice from my previous research on erotic Arab literature. The practice of a man rubbing his manhood against a woman's genitalia to induce an orgasm was documented by Arab erotologists in the sixteenth century. Egyptian Muslim polymath and erotic writer, Jalal al-Din al-Suyuti describes the orgasm-inducing tapping / rubbing practice in his book on Arab-Muslim erotica;

> take her legs and throw her on her back,
> and then rub your penis against her vagina.

---

[20] Brendler, J., 'Sexual Myths and Realities in Brazil,' in Hall, S., and Graham, C., *The Cultural Context of Sexual Pleasure and Problems,* pp. 251-252

Although the kunyaza practice of clitoral stimulation with the penis head is not exclusive to Rwanda, the sexual history, culture and traditions of the East African nation fascinated me. The country's sex-positive attitude towards female pleasure and the pivotal role women played in teaching female sexuality impressed me. The cultural impact of Rwanda's sexual traditions on neighbouring African countries has also received little research in the field of human sexuality. Long before a European 'discovered' the G-Spot in 1950 which was named by two American researchers in 1982, Africans spoke at length about the various female erogenous areas, though it was not documented in written form as many east African cultures were oral cultures.

Why I Wrote This Book

I wanted to write a book to document the sexual history of Rwanda, and help eradicate the stigma surrounding female ejaculation, as well as raise awareness of the kunyaza sexual practice, and its (female) educators. In traditional African cultures, women played an important role in teaching sexual pleasure and dealing with sexual problems. Unfortunately, there has not been much scientific research on the kunyaza technique which has the reputation of triggering female ejaculation.

As I found from my research, female sexuality remains a complex area. However, some research shows that women are capable of experiencing ejaculation with open communication, a good sexual technique, and a relaxed-mindset. Kunyaza is one sexual technique which has proven to be effective for women achieving ejaculation, according to Dr. Nsekuye Bizimana's study. Hopefully this book will serve as a catalyst for further studies on female ejaculation and Rwanda's sexual practice.

Chapter 1: The Pursuit of Pleasure

"Sex is for the woman. Her pleasure is the most important thing." – Felix, Rwandan man

Pleasure is about privilege. Historically, women have rarely had the right to sexual pleasure as they were not in positions of power or their needs were not considered important by those (men) in power. In some cultures, female sexual pleasure is embraced due to the influence of some powerful women. An example of this is the ancient Queen of Rwanda and the kunyaza tradition. Her pursuit of pleasure led to the formation of the Rwandan sexual practice which is also practised in other East and Central African countries. This chapter looks at the origin of Rwanda's pleasure-based tradition, prominent African sex educators and documentaries about kunyaza.

The Origin of Kunyaza in Rwanda

In the Rwanda-Rundi language, kunyaza refers to an ancient sexual practice originating in the Great Lakes region of East Africa. The Great Lakes are a series of lakes constituting part of Africa's Great Rift Valley. Lake Kivu is one of the African Great Lakes. It lies on the border between the Democratic Republic of Congo and the west of Rwanda. Lake Kivu is Rwanda's largest lake and the sixth largest in Africa.

According to legend, kunyaza dates back to the third dynasty rule of the Rwandan monarchy, when the Queen was feeling sexually frustrated whilst her husband, the King, was away on a military campaign. The Queen summoned a guard named Kamagere to make love to her or she'll go crazy. When he refused she commanded, "Do it or be killed." The guard acquiesced and became so anxious about the possible repercussions that he began to shake uncontrollably. Instead of penetrating the Queen, the terrified guard began to repeatedly strike his manhood against the Queen's clitoris. She felt an extremely pleasurable sensation that she had never previously experienced with her husband. The striking made the water spring from her loins. Upon the King's return, the Queen instructed him to perform the striking / tapping motion on her.

Another version of the legend states that the kunyaza practice began with the Queen herself. When the King had gone off to war, the Queen was alone.

She began to touch herself and the water sprang. When the King returned, she showed him how to tap for her to reach an orgasm and ejaculation. She shared this knowledge as penetration was not the only thing she wanted.

The copious flood of the Queen is also said to have started Lake Kivu where people bathe in and claim it's the "fountain of life." The 'water' which gushed from the Queen was called *kunyara*, and the tapping technique which brought about the expulsion became known as *kunyaza*.

Since then, the kunyaza tradition has evolved over time, incorporating various sex positions, herbal aphrodisiacs, and the controversial practice of gukuna (labia pulling) to enhance sexual pleasure. The tradition has orally been passed down from generation to generation by ssengas (paternal aunts), who taught the technique to young girls and women prior to marriage. Kunyaza is now seen as part of Rwandan culture as one woman explained in the *Sacred Water* documentary,

> Kunyaza? It is a cultural habit, men love it. It's a common and widespread part of Rwandan culture. I think all Rwandans do it. It's part of our culture.

Other African countries such as Kenya, Uganda, Burundi, Namibia, Tanzania, and the Democratic Republic of Congo also practice the Rwandan sexual technique. Ironically, the kunyaza tradition began from an illicit encounter and is now practised to maintain marital relationships. Ssengas report that one of the purposes of kunyaza is to prevent infidelity and preserve women's chastity.

The Biblical and Qur'anic story of Prophet Joseph and Potiphar's wife (known as Zulaikha in the Muslim tradition)[21] is similar to the kunyaza legend. In the former, Potiphar's wife unsuccessfully attempted to seduce Joseph, her husband's handsome slave, in her house. The kunyaza legend also involves a powerful married woman initiating a sexual encounter with a young handsome man. Potiphar's wife and the Queen of Rwanda, were both in positions of power and longed for a man who could satisfy them. They also

---

[21] The Biblical story of Prophet Joseph and Potiphar's wife is related in Genesis 39:5-20. In the Qur'an, the story of Prophet Yusuf and the wife of Aziz (Zulaikha) in chapter 12 verses 12-52.

28

had sexual agency. Both stories serve as moralistic tales illustrating the importance of female satisfaction in the lives of married women.

Where is Rwanda?

For those wondering, where is Rwanda? Rwanda is a sovereign state in Central and East Africa. It is one of the smallest countries on the African mainland with a population of approximately 13 million people. Rwanda lies a few degrees south of the Equator, in the heart of Africa. Located in east-central Africa, the country is bordered by Uganda, Tanzania, Burundi and the Democratic Republic of Congo.

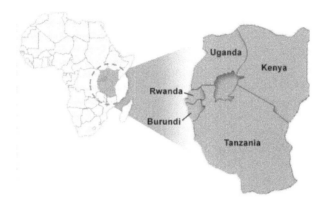

The country is best known for its 480-strong mountain gorilla population, national parks and the government-sponsored genocide in the mid-1990s in which 800,000 people were killed in 100 days. Despite the brutal legacy of violence against women in which up to 500,000 women were reportedly raped during the 1994 genocide between the Hutu and Tutsi ethnic groups, the tiny East African nation has defied expectations in recent years to become a paradigm of gender equality and female empowerment. It boasts the greatest share of women in national government in the world and is home to kunyaza, the inducement of female ejaculation. Unlike other African nations, female genital mutilation (FGM) is not commonly practised in Rwanda.

Ssengas and African Sex Educators

Ssengas are pleasure-positive sex educators teaching about the enjoyment of pleasurable sex. They encourage their female students to have good sex and provide advice on a range of intimate issues. Modern-day ssengas now teach the importance of sexual consent, female agency and women initiating sexual contact. Ssengas also work as marriage counsellors, sex therapists and relationship advisers. A male ssenga is referred to as *kojja* in Uganda.

A number of ssengas also carry out pleasure-orientated sex discussion women-only workshops in a safe space where the female students feel comfortable to ask and speak about sex without judgement. Girls and women would seek advice and confide in their ssengas, on a range of intimate subjects, from their genital appearance to lovemaking tips. Sometimes teaching in the middle of a forest, ssengas advise young and curious women on how to take care of their genitalia and enhance pleasure using herbs.[22] Other ssengas use radio shows to provide sex education and advice, and there are those who use social media to teach people about female sexuality. Challenging cultural taboos in conservative Tanzania, Hindu Shaabani says;

> Sex is a delicate topic and that makes people shy away from talking; yet it is very important in marriage. I have come across women who have been married for over 30 years but have never known the joy of sex in marriage...My job is to challenge our mentality on sex and the culture of silence around the subject. People need to know that they are not the first to experience challenges on the marital bed and so they should seek help.

The ssenga business has been commercialised in recent times as many women outside of Africa travel to the continent to learn from ssengas. Nowadays, ssengas act more like professional sex consultants and relationship counsellors. Ugandan academic, Sylvia Tamale, explored the changing role of ssengas in her research;

> Today's ssengas include both 'conservative' elements that refuse to bend from centuries-old practices and 'progressive' ones that move with the times...The age and education of the ssenga seem to be the influencing factor here, with younger, more highly educated ssengas leaning towards more liberal views than their older, less educated counterparts.

Generally, ssengas do not provide services to unmarried women involved in pre-marital relations as sex is considered only for marriage between heterosexual couples in conservative African communities. That being said,

---

[22] Women in Surinam, in northeast South America, are known to use leaves to cleanse their private parts, as well as herbs to maintain a youthful genital appearance.

Tamale believes that the ssenga enforces female autonomy and agency in ordinary African women;

> For instance, a ssenga would encourage her nieces to engage in some home industry or economic ventures in order to avoid total dependence on her husband...The ssenga also made it clear that a wife did not have to tolerate an abusive spouse; that she had the right to *kunoba* [leave the marriage].

Importance of Sexual Satisfaction in Marriage

Ssengas warn women that if they are not able to perform well in the bedroom, it may lead to their husbands looking elsewhere for satisfaction. Other ssengas teach the importance of female pleasure. Sexual enjoyment is not just for men, ssengas teach. Men should be taught how to pleasure women too. Tanzanian ssenga Hindu Shaabani says,

> It (sex) is a very important aspect of marriage. Every party in a marriage should have a vote and a voice when it comes to sex. It is not just something for men to enjoy; women should too.

According to traditional African sex researchers, heterosexual relationships within marriage, whether monogamous or polygynous, can be just as sexually gratifying, providing that there is mutual respect, trust and communication between the man and his wife. "The secret to a good marriage is good sex," says Kenyan lifestyle designer on sex and relationship. Getrude Mungai. Ugandan sex educator and ssenga, Eunice Okello, adds,

> It (sex) is very important aspect of marriage, and people should stop suffering in silence or hiding problems under the rug. If a woman learns how to please her husband, he will give her everything she wants.

Modern Ssengas and African Sex Educators

There is a growing number of ssengas and African sex educators who are challenging the taboo topic of sex in their respected conservative countries. Notable male and female sex educators make use of various disciplines and mediums to educate people about sexual health and pleasure, particularly women's pleasure, within an African context. Below are some brief accounts of eight notable sex ssengas educators teaching kunyaza/kachabali and the importance of female pleasure.

Vestine Dusabe – Rwandan Sex Educator of Gukuna

Radio personality and sex educator from Kigali, Rwanda, Vestine Dusabe, is a popular advocate of gukuna and kunyaza in Africa. Dusabe visits schools to teach girls about the importance of preserving their chastity and their right to sexual pleasure when they get married. She also hosts an award-winning Rwandan radio show on Flash FM tackling relationship counselling and sex education. Dusabe's willingness to speak openly and frankly about sensitive subjects has helped turn her radio program, *Zirara Zubakwa* ('happy couples'), into one of Rwanda's most popular radio shows since it was launched in 2010. "There are other shows that will discuss sex, but they don't talk about how to have sex," explains Dusabe. "We take calls and try to solve our listeners' sexual problems." The programme was launched after Dusabe became aware of her own aunt's tumultuous relationship. "She used to tell me there was no romance in her relationship," she recounts.

> Her husband would be too rough—the sex was too painful—but she didn't know how to tell him to stop. There was nobody for her to talk to.

Experienced in the art of love, Dusabe travels across East and Central Africa, visiting villages and schools to talk about sexual health and female pleasure using traditional Rwandan sexual practices such as gukuna and kunyaza. A strong advocate for labia pulling, Dusabe fears that modern Western culture will erase some of Rwanda's traditional cultural practices. She also teaches Rwandan men and women about their sexual cultural heritage.

In addition, she teaches women how to pleasure their husbands and criticises men who aren't able to satisfy their wives because they are not skilled in the art of kunyaza. In 2016, Dusabe was featured in Olivier Jourdain's documentary film *Sacred Water*, where she was the film's protagonist. Dusabe also featured in a German documentary about Rwanda as well as the French current affairs radio station, RFI, to speak about her sexually empowering work.

Nsekuye Bizimana, Rwandan Sex Researcher

Born in 1949 in Rwanda, Dr. Nsekuye Bizimana, travelled to Germany in 1970 to study medicine after graduating from a college in Kigali, Rwanda. In 1989, Bizimana authored *White Paradise Hell for Africa?*, a book about the challenges black Africans face in modern-day Europe. In the book Bizimana also spoke about the Rwandan sexual practice of gukuna which has been condemned by the Christian Church. The German-based sex researcher of Rwandan descent, Dr. Nsekuye Bizimana, went on to author two books in French and German about the sexual practice of kunyaza which raised the awareness of the technique in Europe.

In 2010, human sexuality journal *Sexologies* published Bizimana's research in an English article for sexual health professionals called, *Another way for lovemaking in Africa: Kunyaza, a traditional sexual technique for triggering female orgasm at heterosexual encounters.* The author described and critically analysed the characteristics of the kunyaza technique, which reportedly helps women expel large quantities of fluid during orgasms. When asked about why he carried out his research, Bizimana says;

> I simply want women to climax when they make love.

Betty Katana Nalongo, Ugandan Ssenga

Ugandan ssenga, Betty Katana Nalongo, teaches women in her village, the kachabali technique to ensure a healthy sex life. From the Baganda tribe in Uganda, Nalongo was subject to a documentary piece by a Kenyan journalist who interviewed her in Kampala, Uganda, which aired on the Dutch public broadcaster, VPRO for the Metropolis TV Show. Speaking about her role as a ssenga, Nalongo says;

> In my community a ssenga must take on many roles.
> I advise brides-to-be.
> It's my task to ensure married couples live in harmony.

A satisfying sex life, for both the husband and wife is an important component of a good marriage in traditional Baganda culture. Women often visit ssenga Nalongo to learn some of her 'bedroom secrets.' For intense orgasms, women must make sure "the penis rubs against the clitoris of the woman," Nalongo advises women; the importance of shaking the buttocks during sexual activity, making groaning noises, and psychological preparation before engaging in any sexual encounter. Nalongo says,

> Every woman wants to know about sex. Whenever we have a
> problem, we end up talking about sex.

According to Nalongo, clitoral stimulation and a long inner labia are essential for women to reach a mind-blowing orgasm. She advises women to stretch their labia to help facilitate the elusive 'wet orgasm':

> Please ladies take my word. Start to pull [your labia] now. Because it's the only thing which can make you happy in your marriage. It can help you get an orgasm!

Ali Kakonge Simba, Ugandan Sex Herbalist

In western Uganda, Ali Kakonge Simba was introduced from an early age to his two passions; herbs and sex. The former came from his grandfather, who was a well-known herbalist, and the latter from the farmers with whom he would toil every day. "Those guys were always talking about sex and this thing called kunyara (ejaculation)," he recounts. "Listening to them would keep me erect all day." When Simba was 16 he met and made to love a 28-year-old woman, in which he first experienced the joys of kunyaza. As the farmers had counselled, he tried rubbing his penis against her clitoris, as a means to make the woman kunyara (ejaculate). "But she told me that I was doing it all wrong," he explains,

> She taught me how to beat the clitoris slowly. She told me, 'Now you're becoming a man.'

The experience stayed with Simba, and with time and some guidance from his aunt, he was eventually able to combine his two interests and became a sex herbalist. Nowadays, Simba teaches the kunyaza technique to couples and sells his homemade aphrodisiac called Vetexine – a hormone booster to help women squirt the 'water.' According to Simba, the most important thing is that the woman ultimately reaches "her destination" he explains. "Then your woman will never leave or cheat on you. She will even tell you all her secrets." A man's ability to execute kunyaza effectively and make a woman expel 'water' is considered a proof of manliness, according to Simba. "It's what makes a man, a man!" He continues,

> When you're doing the kunyaza you [should] brush the penis over the vagina, mostly on the clitoris. She will feel it nicely and she will start releasing water. That's what they call kunyara. It's what women enjoy most. I also enjoy it when I'm doing it because when I am with a woman who is dry, I feel pain... It's the sound that comes out of the kunyaza style is what makes me and other men happy.... When you see that water coming out you feel that you've done it, you feel that you are also a [real] man.

Getrude Mungai - Kenyan Sexologist

Lifestyle designer on sex and relationship, Getrude Mungai is a popular figure in the field of sexuality in Kenya. A TV presenter, writer and radio personality, Mungai draws upon her years of studies and experience, to raise awareness about sexuality and promote female pleasure in an African context, particularly for married women,

> Born and raised on the Kenyan coast. I am privileged to be born and raised in the Rabai community from the Kenyan coast. Rabais prepares girls from puberty on the realities of sex and intimacy in marriage. The basics of my knowledge is a wealth of African traditional culture. This knowledge is from various tribes and communities in East Africa and beyond. I have also travelled extensively and learned from my visits. From the Indians the art of Kama Sutra and the secret of the Middle East from a Harlem trainer. I constantly keep abreast of developments in the sex and intimacy field and read widely. With knowledge from the West and East plus experiences and practical experiments in my own marriage, the end product is a customized and tailor-made product for our modern African society.

Somewhat of a cultural icon in Kenya, Mungai has popularised terms such as 'Mr Victor,' referring to the penis, 'Ms Victoria,' referring to the vagina and 'Mombasa Raha,'[23] referring to sexual activities and techniques. In 2013, one of her Mombasa Raha tutorial videos on sex positions went 'viral' online, attracting millions of viewers. The married, mother of two grew in popularity after the video was released. Described as Kenya's leading sexologist, Mungai has been advising married couples for decades on how to maintain an enjoyable sex life. She provides intimacy courses for women in small private classes on how to entice their husbands as well as ensuring their desires are met.

Not afraid of public backlash, a committed Christian, Mungai self-identifies as a 'sexologist' in conservative Kenya, where she has experienced hostility from some quarters as Kenyans asked, "why would anyone want to make a career out of teaching others how to have good sex?" Equally confident as she is defiant, Mungai is aware of the scepticism that many Africans have about her line of work and the stigma she receives from some parents. Some mothers and schools do not even want her speaking to students out of fear

---

[23] Mombasa is a city on the coast of Kenya.

that they will engage in pre-martial relationships. A supporter of sexual abstinence until marriage, Mungai responded,

> I am not only a professional, I am also a mother and the last thing I would do is teach children the art of making love – I am a firm believer that sex belongs in marriage, however, the fact is that our children are having it, and someone needs to give them a sober talk about irresponsible sex.

According to Mungai, active female participation is crucial for women to fully enjoy intimate relations. She encourages women not to simply lay down and "let the man do all the work." She reminds her female students, many of whom aren't married, not to deny the importance of having a healthy sexual relationships when married, "The majority of married women downplay sex, they get married and they settle." Similar to other sex educators in Africa, Mungai advises women on the importance of being confident and adventurous in the bedroom:

> There is a very thin line between being a nice woman [in bed] and being a boring woman in bed...As a hot woman in bed, you don't pump, men pump! We shake [our hips and buttocks]!

Valentine Njoroge, Kenyan Feminist Sex Writer

Sex and feminist sex writer, Valentine Njoroge hosts an online show called *Ask Valentine*, to 'awaken African sexuality.' In her show, she answers people's sex questions and also examines societal attitudes and perceptions about sex, and how they affect people's lives. A self-proclaimed feminist, Njoroge tackles women's issues in contemporary Kenya, challenges traditional relationship and says that "talking about sex is easily the biggest taboo (in Kenya)." Njoroge continues,

> The other big taboo is female orgasm. In a patriarchal and highly chauvinistic society, female sexual pleasure is not really discussed or prioritised. Some men think I am being pushy and demanding something that is 'un-African'. While others are happy and willing to become better lovers.

A strong campaigner for women's rights, Njoroge sees her work as a form of female empowerment, whereby she wants to help African women prioritise their own pleasure in the bedroom. She argues that sex education in Kenya concentrates on teaching women how to pleasure a man and prevent men from cheating;

> One of things I think I bring to being a sex writer is looking at female pleasure and us prioritising ourselves, and setting the tone in our own bedrooms.

Njoroge co-hosts *Konnect* on K24, a TV program on sex and relationship, with co-host Kenyan sexologist, Getrude Mungai. The light-hearted talk show addresses a range of topics from sex positions, to the female orgasm, to premature ejaculation. The entertaining duo also speak about dating, marriage and sex from the perspective of Mungai, a conservative married woman, and Njoroge, a liberal unmarried woman. Although they often have opposing views, both Mungai and Njoroge are committed to promoting female sexuality and pleasure for African women. Njoroge is also a panellist on *The She Word*, an TV programme produced by BBC Africa.

Maurice Matheka, Kenyan Sex Therapist

After obtaining a degree in IT and management in the UK, Maurice Matheka from Kenya came across a course in sexology to understand people's social dynamics and psychology. His interest sparked as he went on to study gender psychology before becoming a certified sex therapist in 2002. Now a leading sexologist and gender psychologist in his native Kenya, Matheka teaches relationship dynamics, cultural attitudes towards sex and provides information about sexual techniques based on scientific research. Matheka provides therapy sessions on relationship issues, in which his core passion is "about liberating women and men on the art of satisfactory sex."

Kenya is a multi-ethnic, multi-cultural and multi-faith country, in which there are people who are very conservative and those that are very liberal. With regards to the matters of sex, Mathekha is well aware of the stigma some people have about his work and wants to address the taboo of sex in Kenya. He also aims to tackles some misconceptions people have about Kenyan men such as the idea which some Kenyan women say that Nigerian and Ugandan men are better lovers than Kenyan men. According to Matheka,

> Nigerian and Ugandan men are man enough to show affection in public and have that male prowess, whereas a Kenyan man would be timid depending on who he is with.

37

According to Matheka, Kenyans are more promiscuous than other Africans, but they hide their sexual encounters due to societal pressures to be conservative. Matheka has attracted much attention inside Kenya after his sex tutorial video on 'how to make her squirt' was published online. In the video, Matheka demonstrates inducing large amounts of fluid in less than two minutes, by stimulating the woman's G-Spot with his fingers.

Angelica Lindsey-Ali, American Muslim Sexual Health Educator

Certified sexual health educator Angelica Lindsey-Ali, also known as 'The Village Auntie' is a kunyaza expert and lecturer who offers practical advice and resources for "reconnecting women with traditional African femininity and sexuality from an Islamic perspective." An American Muslim of African and Mexican descent, Lindsey-Ali hosts women-only workshops on traditional African practices including kunyaza. The Village Auntie challenges her female students to re-examine the critical role of woman-to-woman communication as well as age-grade societies as a tool for dissemination of not only practical sexual knowledge but as a portal for the modelling of femininity, positive body image, and the rightful role of women as pillars of family and community. Lindsey-Ali says,

> As a black woman born and raised in Detroit, I came up in a community that taught me to speak the unspeakable, do the impossible, and speak for the forgotten. Muslim women are often shamed when we establish a sense of agency over their bodies. I want to help change that.

A native of Detroit, in the state of Michigan, Lindsey-Ali is a committed Muslim and community scholar whose research interests include the West African roots of African American Islamic identity and the role of sacred sexuality within West and East African cultures. After spending years abroad in the Middle East and West Africa learning about Islam and African cultures from ssengas, Lindsey-Ali is reviving traditional African traditions to black and brown women in the United States. Inspired by female sex educators in African villages, Lindsey-Ali aims to revive the role of the ssenga tradition to the Americas where she introduces women from different ethnic backgrounds and religions to traditional African beauty and sexual practices such as kunyaza, vaginal steaming, African waistbeads, *qasil* (soap leaf), *huruud* (turmeric) and twerk dancing.

In 2018, Lindsey-Ali launched an initiative called *Reclaiming the Village Auntie: Exploring African Femininity & Sexuality from an Islamic Perspective*, to educate and empower women on sexuality and sensuality. Lindsey-Ali's work has earned much praise for her willingness to destigmatise female sexuality. A trailblazer in the field of traditional African sexuality in the United States, Lindsey-Ali has garnered much praise for her workshops and retreats on sexual health and female pleasure. An unapologetically black, Muslim, *hijab* (headscarf)-wearing, female sex educator, Angelica Lindsey-Ali's work on sexual self-care for women is much needed, especially in black and Muslim communities where talking about sex is taboo. Helping women overcome sexual trauma and embrace their femininity, Lindsey-Ali regularly uses social media to inform and educate women about pleasure, with her tag-line, "Get that O sis!" Explaining why she joined the social media networking service Twitter, Lindsey-Ali said,

> I want to prove that sex isn't haram (forbidden in Islam) and seeking pleasure is a woman's right. Because not all of us are prudes. And too many women are experiencing an epidemic of bad sex. I'm a sexual health educator and I want to help change that.

Kunyaza and Kachabali in the Media

In recent times, many Westerners have studied African cultures and sexuality to gain a better understanding of male-female relations within an African context. An example is Canadian journalist, Matthew Stein, who authored a number of published articles on the sexual practices and dating customs of Rwanda and Uganda. Stein's articles are an "attempt to promote a cultural understanding for his Western readers concerning sexual practices and relationships in East Africa." The Rwandan culture of female ejaculation is one of Stein's most popular pieces. A white Canadian man, Stein admitted his ignorance of female ejaculation until he moved to East Africa,

> For most of my sexual life, female ejaculation didn't register on my bedroom to-do list. It proved an elusive mystery, and like many Western men, I was content to stay ignorant ... and dry. Then I moved to tiny Rwanda, where I encountered a culture that embraces female ejaculation — or *kunyara*, as it's known locally — with unprecedented vigor. Here men seek out women who look "heavy"; banana fiber mats are offered as engagement gifts, to protect mattresses; and herbal concoctions are available to help women produce more "water."

Due to the 'bad sex' epidemic in the West, many Western women have turned to the East in their pursuit of pleasure. Yoga and tantric sex are two eastern traditions now widely practised by European and American women to solve their sexual problems. There is also a growing interest in Western women looking to Africa to aid their sexual malaise. Traditional African practices such as kunyaza is gaining attention by more women in the West for its reputation of inducing female ejaculation and orgasms. This has caused a rise in commercial interest in the tradition. Some Africans have accused ssengas and Western people of exploiting their sacred traditions for commercial gain. Similar to the 'exploitation' of the Angolan dance *kizomba* which has been misinterpreted from a family-friendly sensual dance to a sexually charged erotic dance in parts of Europe and South America, traditional ssengas want "white people to appreciate their tradition without exploitation and cultural appropriation," a sex educator from Kenya said.

Kunyaza Documentaries

Kunyaza has been the subject of a number of documentary films by European and North American filmmakers such as; *Le Sexe Autour du Monde: Rwanda* (2011) by TV5 Québec in Canada, *Kunyaza - Afrikanische Liebeskunst* (2011) by German erotic film director Pierre Roshan, *Sunny Side of Sex: Uganda* (2012) by Dutch filmmaker Sunny Bergman, *Unter fremden Decken Ruanda* (2014) by German free-to-air television network, ProSieben, and *Sacred Water* (2016) by Belgian filmmaker, Olivier Jourdain. A brief summary of each documentary is presented below;

In the second episode of the 2011 Canadian documentary series *Le Sexe Autour de Monde* (Sex around the World), broadcasted by TV5 Canada, journalist Philippe Desrosiers visits Rwanda to investigate gukuna (labia pulling) and kunyaza (also spelt, *kunyasa*). In the one-hour documentary, Desrosiers also explores Rwandan sexual attitudes and culture where a number of inner-city Rwandans said that gukuna and kunyaza were outdated practices.

German erotic educational film *Kunyaza – Afrikanische Liebeskunst* (Kunyaza – African Love Art) released in 2011, was one of the first videos to explicitly depict how the kunyaza technique is practised. The film begins with a female voiceover narrating;

> When it comes to ancient traditional sex techniques, most people think of the Indian Kamasutra. Few people are likely to know that a love tradition has existed in Africa for centuries. The basics are taught in this film.

The sex educational film is also called *Kunjasa* in a number of pornographic sites. The erotic film attracted a lot of interest outside of Africa and was widely shared online. Whilst the Rwandan sexual practice proved to be very popular amongst visitors to pornographic sites, very few sex researchers and sexual health professionals investigated the practice.

In the four-part documentary series, *Sunny Side of Sex*, Dutch filmmaker Sunny Bergman takes a positive look at sexuality, femininity and love in various countries. In one of the films, Bergman explores the attitudes to female sexuality and the kachabali tradition in Uganda. The film follows Ugandan professional ssengas, who teach women how to please their husbands and enhance their own sexual pleasure. Bergman visits a Ugandan ssenga's house, where the sex educator demonstrates the labia pulling practice on the filmmaker as she lays on the bed. The ssenga later explains to Bergman that the labia pulling practice between females is not a homoerotic practice. Homosexuality is socially unacceptable and illegal in Uganda and other parts of Africa.[24]

In one scene, Bergman joins a class of Ugandan school children being taught the importance of sexual pleasure in a marital relationship. One of the students, a young *hijab* (headscarf)-wearing Muslim girl, rises to her feet to eloquently explain the importance of the kachabali tradition for married women in Ugandan culture. Bergman also found that many of the women in rural Uganda were content with their sexuality. They seemed very confident with their bodies and were proud of their elongated labia. Bergman remarked;

---

[24] The self-identified exclusively homosexual/gay individual is an artefact of Western society. In most African societies, homosexuality is considered a choice and not a biological reality. According to president of Kenya, Uhuru Kenyatta, gay rights are "of no importance to the people of Kenya." Ugandan president, Yoweri Museveni, passed the Anti-Homosexuality Act, 2014, saying "no study has shown you can be homosexual by nature." Rwandan Dr. Nsekuye Bizimana said most Rwandans did not know about homosexuality until they came into contact with Europeans and Americans. Bizimana wrote that "homosexuality is a phenomenon of decadence associated with affluence." According to Kenyatta, Museveni and Bizimana, most Kenyans, Ugandans and Rwandans do not consider homosexuality to be an acceptable practice in their respective cultures.

> We (Europeans) went there to find out what we could learn from them (Africans) about sex, usually it's the other way around.

Unter fremden Decken Ruanda (Under Strange Rwanda Blankets), a 2014 German documentary on Rwanda's sexual traditions reported that Rwandan women are the most sexually satisfied women in the world. The documentary film features sex journalists Paula Lambert and Thilo Mischke who travel to different countries on an erotic mission "in search for the best sex in the world." In the Rwanda episode, Mischke travels to the city of Kigali to learn about kunyaza, gukuna, and Rwandan's secret to satisfying women in the bedroom. Rwandan sexologist, Vestine Dusabe, nurse Claudine Batamuriza and sex herbalist, Ali Kakonge Simba were all interviewed. The documentary also includes testimonies from men and women from Rwanda, Germany, Cuba, Colombia, Russia, Spain, Turkey, France and the United States on the effectiveness of the kunyaza technique.

The documentary reported that up to 80% of Rwandan women regularly experience orgasms. In contrast, it reported that 52% of Spanish women, 44% of Brazilian women, 36% of American women, 33% of German, and 11% of Japanese women regularly experience orgasms during sexual encounters. Rwanda's traditional sex-positive culture and sexual practices were cited as the main reasons why Rwandan women orgasm more frequently than other women around the world.

Demonstrating the kunyaza technique using a cucumber and a watermelon, sexologist Vestine Dusabe teaches journalist Mischke, how Rwandan men help women ejaculate. Prolonged clitoral stimulation with the penis and patience from the man is required to effectively perform kunyaza so that "women can release the water." Dusabe also explains the active role women play by laying on her back with her legs widely opened, or by rotating her buttocks whilst she is on all fours during sexual play.

Olivier Jourdain, the Belgian filmmaker behind the documentary *Sacred Water*, was a novice to the world of ejaculation when he first visited Rwanda in 2009. He learned of the kunyaza custom a month into his stay, after coming across a wet mattress outside a friend's home. Jourdain's friend "explained the history in such a poetic way," recounts the filmmaker. "It wasn't pornographic. It wasn't the American way of squirting." As his curiosity piqued. Jourdain read widely, and later met Vestine Dusabe, the charismatic Rwandan sexologist and host of a radio programme about sex education and relationship counselling. Dusabe went on to become the film's protagonist.

In *Sacred Water*, individual men and women, teenage girls and couples frankly discuss women's orgasms and pleasure in the humorous yet informative film. Men see women's ejaculation as sign of their prowess, and a way to make sure they are pleasuring their partners. Women say they enjoy "pouring water" and that "finding the water" guards against infidelity. According to kunyaza practitioners, both partners should enjoy pleasure. In one scene, a woman visits the office of sexual herbalist, Ali Kakonge Simba. After the woman complains that her "water has dried up," Simba suggests that her husband should perform kunyaza on her. He compares good sexual skills to playing a guitar and says "making love is like playing soccer. You need fair play so that both sides can score."

Despite its erotic heritage, talking about sex is taboo in most parts of Rwanda which largely remains a conservative country. The film also alludes to the ongoing debate on whether or not the country's sexual practices are outdated. Girls learn about the practice of gukuna and some wonder if it is a sin. Since its 2016 release, *Sacred Water* has been screened in several film festivals around the world and won several awards. The director attributes the film's success to its universal theme of female pleasure. Jourdain said,

> I wanted to share the fascination I felt when discovering the subject myself. I was amazed to discover a culture of sexuality in Rwanda, opposed to our Western approach, which is usually much more individual. Were we talking about some kind of African Kama Sutra? I also wanted to show another view on Rwanda, something that was reuniting and encompassing the whole country. A positive film about a country that has lived through horror twenty years ago.[25]

Masculinity and Femininity in East Africa

In Kinyarwanda, a Rwandan language, a man is called *umugabo*, which is derived from the verb (*kugaba*) to provide. This indicates that the primary responsibility of a man is to be a provider. In a focus group discussion undertaken in Rwanda, respondents underscored a man's ability to take care

---

[25] Referring to the 1994 genocide in Rwanda.

of – and provide for – his wife and children as the essential features of a 'real man.' Often such traits in a man would be expressed through the idiom of respect (*icyubahiro*) rather than through the idiom of love (*urukundo*). The idiom of respect is of a wide-ranging nature; it involves the obligation of a man to show respect (*kubaha*) towards his wife and children, so that he can also earn the respect (*icyubahiro*) of other people, who recognise a man's ability to give and provide for his family.

Although there is a strong emphasis on the ability of men to provide, this does not mean that people identified material wealth as the defining feature of a 'real man'. Respondents spoke of personal traits such as honesty and determination as the defining features of a 'real man,' while a few people pointed to material wealth or status, as the basis of manhood.

A 'Real Man' in Africa

Traditionally across African cultures, a 'real man' is a man who provides financially, emotionally and physically for his wife and family. The concept of a husband being a provider, encompasses providing for the psychologically and emotional needs of his wife. In some African cultures it is considered a sign of virility for men to have many sexual partners. Conversely, a large number of sexual partners for women is considered evidence of sexual promiscuity and is linked to a questionable social status.[26] However male virility is praised when exercised through marriage (monogamy or polygamy). For example, a man who has multiple casual female lovers, known as a philanderer, womanizer or ladies' man, is not respected in traditional African cultures. In comparison, a man who has multiple wives is respected for his ability to look after and satisfy them.

In the context of a husband, a 'real man' provides for the needs of his wife (or wives), both physical and psychological. In the African context, a sexually satisfied wife is crucial to maintaining a good marital relationship. In a field study, one male respondent said that African men are expected to take care of their wife's needs or else they are not considered to be a 'real man.' Sexual satisfaction is extremely important in a relationship according to African sex columnist, Valentine Njoroge;

---

[26] Brendler, J., 'Sexual Myths and Realities in Brazil,' in Hall, K, and Graham, C, *The Cultural Context of Sexual Pleasure and Problems*, pp. 251-252

What makes a romantic relationship special is sex. We can live with, share money with and even love other people. What marks a romantic relationship as special and separate is sex.

"Marriage Needs Good Sex"

Senior lecturer of women and gender studies in Kampala, Uganda, Dr. Florence Kyoheirwe Muhanguzi carried out in-depth interviewed and focus group discussions with heterosexual married women on female sexuality. In the 2015 study of sexual desire and pleasure amongst Ugandan women, Muhanguzi found that all of the women expressed the view that sex was a valued aspect of a successful and happy marriage. Accordingly, women noted that "sex is sweet, when there is no sex there is no marriage," "it is enjoyable," "you feel good and relaxed." The women associated "good" and satisfying sex with stable relationships. In one focus group discussion, one woman said;

> Sex is important for our lives. You feel good. The man needs a touch, he also feels good. The relationship between husband and wife depends on the quality of sex. If there is no sex, there are frequent quarrels and fights at home. There is no peace.

"Kunyaza is for the Wife"

For some men, kunyaza serves as a relationship signifier. Some men will only perform the technique on their wife. The mentality of such men is that only a woman he really cares for "deserves special attention." A female sexual partner that he doesn't care for, i.e. a prostitute or casual lover, doesn't warrant such effort as her pleasure is not a priority, according to one male respondent. A 49-year-old Rwandan prison guard explains;

> Kunyaza is more appropriate for the wife, since it is feeling, loving and caring. It's being attentive. When it comes to the commercial sex worker, she just wants another customer. It's all about economy. 1,000 – 2,000 after the first round you pay, but with kunyaza it takes time to come and it delays your ejaculation, so you might double the bill by doing kunyaza with a prostitute.

Is Kunyaza an African Tantra?

Tantric sex, or tantra as its often known, is a sensual practice with roots in Hinduism, Buddhism, Taoism and Jainism. Tantra requires and teaches the important elements of sacred sensuality, including; connection with the heart in sexual union, complete comfort with the body, a high level of ability to communicate sexual needs, exceptional skills in the art of lovemaking, physical agility, awareness of how sexual energy feels when it runs through the body, and a willingness to enter into a mystical state. Tantric sex is a slow form of sex that is said to increase intimacy and create a mind-body connection that can lead to powerful full-body orgasms. The ability to integrate tantra teachings and enter higher states of consciousness for long periods grows over time with practise. Tantra is not goal-orientated where the focus is on orgasm. It is ultimately about pleasure.

Tantra lovers take their mind off the *yoni* (vagina) *moolah bandha* (orgasm) and instead focus on making foreplay enjoyable and rewarding by way of a variety of methods including; meditative techniques, breath control, full consciousness and sensual massage, until they are ready to achieve climax. Tantra is said to bring couples closer together emotionally and spiritually by channelling the *kundalini* (dormant sexual energy) through *chakras* (body's energy centres). Meditation, touching, breathing and visualisation is also adopted to develop the sexual energy of tantra sex lovers.

Similar to tantra, kunyaza sex is a sexual practice which includes slow penetration to increase intimacy and create an emotionally connection between lovers. The Rwandan practice of kunyaza shares some of the principles of the ancient Indian practice of tantra, according to tantra teachers. For example, American tantra teacher and author of *S.O.L. Sacred Orgasmic Living,* Shophar Graves, made mention of the shared principles of tantra sex and kunyaza in an online radio show for *Fo-Sho Holistic Health.* Brazilian tantra practitioner and founder of *Full Life Academy*, Henrique Utsch, also recognised the similarities between the two ancient sexual traditions. American blogger and tantra author, Jennifer Lawless referred to kunyaza as the 'African Secret to Ultimate Female Orgasm,' on her website, citing American sex writer Svetlana Ivanova who also wrote about the Rwandan sex technique. Others have described kunyaza as 'Africa's Kama Sutra' and the 'African tantra.' For many sex educators, tantra sex like kunyaza sex starts in the mind.

Chapter 2: The Psychology of Female Desire and Kunyaza

"Open communication increases the chances of your libido bouncing back."
– Dr. Cynthia Graham, professor in sexual and reproductive health

Research shows that sexual desire in women is more complex and more fragile than it is in men. It's less tied to biology, and more linked to psychology. Researchers state that women have higher erotic plasticity than men. Erotic plasticity is the theory that sexual desire and preferences can change based on external socio-cultural factors. In regard to kunyaza, the practice will not be effective unless a woman is psychologically prepared and aroused for sexual play. This chapter presents an insight into women's emotions, female libido studies and practical tips to get aroused.

Understanding Women's Emotions

The psychological aspect of sex is far more important than the physical aspect of sex in the female arousal process. Neuropsychological studies have shown that male and female brains are configured differently. Men tend to be aroused by visual sexual stimuli, whereas women tend to be aroused when they feel secure and are mentally at ease. Relaxation and concentration help a woman's brain process the pleasures her body is experiencing during love play, thus increasing the joy of physical relations. It cannot be over emphasised the importance of a woman being in a loving state of mind to fully enjoy kunyaza or any other sexual practice. An experienced practitioner from Rwanda said;

> You have to talk to her first, then you caress each other. You have to feel at ease. Don't rush, take your time. If you want to do kunyaza, you have to control your excitement. Go easy.

Many men fail miserably in understanding women's emotions before engaging sexual play. A woman's emotions and mind should be relaxed and at ease before engaging in any form of sexual play, sex educators advise. It is not uncommon for women to express the need for emotional connection before they want to make love. A man can establish an emotional connection when he pays attention, shows empathy, and is responsive to her needs. This should prelude any form of physical touch.

Women tend to think more about the romantic process of emotional intimacy, rather than actual act of penetration. In fact, for many women focusing on the sexual act without the process is a turn off. There is nothing wrong with this way of thinking, it is just different to how man tend to think about sex. The reason for this lies in the biological disposition of the genders. While some women have higher than normal testosterone levels, most do not, which means that most women are not "biologically driven to think about sex like men." For women, it's love, intimacy and romance which tends to drive them to feel sexual and think about sex. The fact that many women tend to be emotionally driven and men tend to be biologically driven to have sex is not an issue providing that there is mutual understanding and a deep appreciation for their differences. We are supposed to complement each other as God intended, not compete with one another.

Female Sexuality and the Female Libido

Female sexuality is culturally relative. History and culture shapes women's sexuality according to sex anthropologist Bella Ellywood-Clayton in her book *Sex Drive: In Pursuit of Female Desire*. For example, a hundred years ago in the West, a woman with a high sex drive was regarded as mentally disturbed, whereas today, a woman who does not express a high sex drive may be diagnosed as sexually dysfunctional. The unrealistic expectations about women's sex drive in today's hypersexual Western society can have a devasting effect on women's sexual self-esteem and relationships. Feeling like they do not live up to the physical ideal, many women often grow to view themselves, and even their genitalia, as undesirable.

The truth is what is 'normal,' 'abnormal' and 'low libido' varies amongst women in difficult cultures. 'Low sexual desire' is actually common amongst many women in long-term monogamous relationships. It is actually normal for a woman to experience a decrease in libido whilst in a stable relationship. Unfortunately, the media, advertising and the medical community have led women to believe that having a 'low libido' means something is inherently wrong with them. They are pathologized as having a type of female sexual dysfunction called hypoactive sexual desire disorder (HSDD). The reality is, as Ellywood-Clayton argues, many of the medical researchers who made this nebulous definition have financial ties to pharmaceutical companies. Women's sexuality is exploited for financial gain, much like how female insecurity is exploited by the beauty industry. Rather than focusing on what is considered 'normal' libido and comparing their libido to other women, it may be beneficial for women to be encouraged to explore and experiment with their own sensuality without censure.

Why Women Lose Interest in Sex

Lack of interest in sex is a common problem for women, especially when a woman is in a long-term relationship. Research pinpoints several factors that may play a role in low libido in women such as; poor physical and mental health, having experienced non-consensual sex at some point in their lives, young children in the household, not sharing the same sexual likes and dislikes as her partner, religious and cultural beliefs, and a lack of emotional connection with her partner.

According to professor of sexual and reproductive health Dr. Cynthia Graham, low sexual interest should be treated very differently for men and women; "Our findings suggest that open communication about sex with partners is linked with a reduced likelihood of having low sexual interest." Lead author of a 2017 study of British sexual attitudes, Graham found that women are more than twice as likely as men to lack interest in sex when living with a partner. It found that while men and women lost sexual passion with age, women lost desire by longer relationships.

Based on the experiences of 6,669 women and 4,839 men aged between 16 and 74 who reported at least one sexual partner in the past year. The 2017 study published in BMJ Open found that overall, 34% of women and 15% of men reported lacking interest in sex. Half of these people, 62% of women and 53% of men said that they were distressed by their lack of interest in sex.[27] The study's authors said that problems of sexual desire should be treated by looking at the person holistically, rather than resorting to anti-depressant

[27] Graham, C., Mercer, C, Tanton, C, *et al.* 'What factors are associated with reporting lacking interest in sex and how do these vary by gender? Findings from the third British national survey of sexual attitudes and lifestyles.'

drugs such as flibanserin.[28] Senior lecturer at the University of Southampton, Dr. Cynthia Graham said,

> Our findings show us the importance of the relational context in understanding low sexual interest in both men and women. For women in particular, the quality and length of relationship and communication with their partners are important in their experience of sexual interest. It highlights the need to assess and – if necessary – treat sexual interest problems in a holistic and relationship, as well as gender-specific way.

For some women, it is natural and completely normal to lose interest in sex, others find it causes pain and misery. Hypoactive sexual desire disorder (HSDD), also known as low libido in women, is a common problem that affects many women at some point in their life. In the West, women are under a great amount of societal pressure to be sexually desirous, have a high sex drive and be sexually active. The truth is many women are not interested in sex as much as they would like, or society expects.

Women turn-off from sex for a variety of reasons, but researchers have found that women who spoke about sex were less likely to experience low libido. Sex therapist Ammanda Major said,

> Sex is a very personal thing, and talking about it can be embarrassing. But talking is often the best thing you can do to improve your sex life.

Flexibility of the Female Libido

Studies have shown that a woman's libido can be influenced by the society and culture in which she resides. The female libido is more responsive to external (socio-cultural) factors than the male libido, according to proponents of the erotic plasticity theory. The theory refers to the degree to which the libido is shaped by social, cultural, and situational (external) factors.

According to the female erotic plasticity theory, women in general have higher erotic plasticity than men, and therefore their libidos are more flexible and responsive to external factors such as religious and cultural attitudes towards female sexuality. A person has 'high erotic plasticity' when their sex

---

[28] Flibanserin is the first-ever medically approved drug aimed at boosting female libido. Approved by the US Food and Drug Administration (FDA), flibanserin is sometimes referred to as the "Pink Viagra" or "the Female Viagra."

drive is greatly influenced by external factors, whereas someone has 'low erotic plasticity' when their sex drive is relatively rigid and less susceptible to change from external factors. Theory and research on sexuality and libido tend to cluster around two very opposing views;

- Nature – The view that biological factors such as genetics determines or influences sexuality, libido and sexual behaviour,
- Nurture – The view that external factors, such as society and culture determines or influences sexuality, libido and sexual behaviour.

There is ample evidence to suggest that women have higher erotic plasticity than men. This is not necessarily either a good or a bad thing, but it may be helpful in understanding sexual differences between the genders. Social psychologist Roy Baumeister proposes that the female sex drive is more malleable than the male in response to sociocultural and situational factors. He argued that there are gender differences in erotic plasticity, meaning that women are more influenced by cultural and social factors than men are. He attributed the gender difference in erotic plasticity to 'evolutionary' and biological forces.

Erotic Plasticity Studies

In 2005, psychologist Meredith Chivers set up an experiment where she showed a variety of erotic videos to self-identified heterosexual and homosexual male and female participants. The videos depicted a wide variety of sexual activities covering various combinations: man/woman, man/man, woman/woman, woman alone, man alone, and animal/animal. The participants' genitals were wired to measure blood flow, indicator of arousal, and the participants were instructed to indicate their arousal level with a keypad.

Most of the male participants' self-reported arousal levels were consistent with the measured blood flow responses. The self-identified heterosexual men were aroused by the naked women images, and the self-identified homosexual men were aroused by the naked men. The mating (bonobos) animals did not arouse any of the men. In addition, the men's self-reported arousal levels matched their genital blood flow to indicate arousal.

In contrast, the self-identified heterosexual and homosexual female participants, responded genitally to everything – even the mating animals. However, the women did not self-report being aroused by some of the videos, despite their blood flows indicating that they were aroused.

In conclusion, Chivers' study found that women tend to become aroused by heterosexual and homosexual erotica, indicating a bisexual arousal pattern. However, this doesn't mean that all of the women are actually bisexual. The results suggest that women are more likely than men to be aroused by sexual and erotic imagery, irrespective of the genders involved.

Another study, led by Dr Gerulf Rieger from the Department of Psychology at the University of Essex, involved 345 women whose responses to being shown videos of naked men and women were analysed. The results, which were based on elements such as whether their pupils dilated in response to sexual stimuli, showed that 82% of the women tested were aroused by both sexes. Meanwhile of the women who identified as heterosexual, 74% were strongly sexually aroused by videos of both attractive men and attractive women. This was in contrast to self-identified lesbians, who showed much stronger sexual responses to women than to men.

Social psychologist Roy Baumeister undertook a meta-study of fifty years of data on sexual differences between men and women. He wrote, "Once a man's sexual tastes emerge, they are less susceptible to change or adaptation than a woman's." Some of the American psychologist's examples were in reports about group sex in which he found;

- women would almost always perform cunnilingus on the other women, but heterosexual men wouldn't perform fellatio on the other men;
- women are more likely to self-identify as bisexual,
- women are more likely than men, to change between heterosexual and homosexual relationships during lifetime; and
- lesbians are more likely than gay men to say their sexual orientation is a "choice."

An erotic plasticity study of animals carried out by Keith Kendrick in 2001 including goats and sheep, showed the same erotic plasticity difference between the male and female animals. In the study baby goats were given at birth to sheep mothers, and lambs were given to goat mothers. They were segregated from any contact with their own species. When they were reproductively mature, the animals were brought into groups of mixed sheep and goats, of both sexes.

The males of both species showed no interest in the females of their own kind. They only wanted to mate with the species they had been raised with: goats with sheep and sheep with goats. Females were different: they would have sex with either species. In other words, erotic plasticity appears to be a phenomenon that extends beyond humans.

Flaws in the Erotic Plasticity Studies

The results from the erotic plasticity studies are not conclusive and it can be argued that it is not a fair representation of understanding erotic plasticity gender differences for the following reasons;

- The sample size of the studies is small;
- Lack of ethnic and cultural diversity of participants;
- Genital arousal and vaginal lubrication does not always indicate consensual arousal in a woman's mind;
- Sexual past and attitudes of the participants may have influenced their responses to the erotic images;
- The analogy of humans and animals is flawed as animals do not have the human capability of discernment; and
- There is no consensus amongst sex researchers on homosexuality in terms of whether or not it's a biological reality.

10 Things To Get You In The Mood

Women require a myriad of things to help them get in the mood. Drawn from the findings of sex educators, psychologists and everyday women, below are ten things women can do to get in the mood for sexual activities.

1. Accept Yourself

"Do not do anything that comprises your view of yourself as a woman," says sexual anthropologist Dr. Bella Ellywood-Clayton. Many women get stuck on the fact that they aren't as young as they used to be or as thin as they would like to be, and ultimately avoid sexual encounters that make them feel vulnerable about their appearance. It is important to not concentrate on your flaws and imperfections and remember that confidence is sexy! Put those negative thoughts aside, and don't let self-consciousness get in the way of enjoying your love life. Sex writer Valentine Njoroge says,

> Your imperfect man wants to have sex with you – perfectly flawed *you*. He wants to express his affection for you with his body and share his imperfections with you. I think that is pretty beautiful frankly. Perfection on the other hand is boring. It's our scars, marks and idiosyncrasies that tell the story of who we are and makes us unique and beautiful.

2. Think Pleasure

The word 'mood' means 'state of mind,' so to get in the mood, you need to concentrate on your most crucial sex organ – the mind. It is possible to think your way to get in the mood. Author of *Sex Drive: In Pursuit of Female Desire*, Dr Bella Ellwood-Clayton says,

> Sensuality, particularly for women, is often about our mindset. If there isn't enough space in our mind to entertain erotic sensibilities, then forget about entertaining an actual penis. Learning what exactly makes us feel sensual is the key to everything.

3. Touch Yourself

Ugandan ssenga Betty Nalongo encourages women to explore their own bodies by masturbating to understand what turns them on, which they can then teach to their male partners during kachabali. Masturbation helps to promote healthy blood flow to the genitals, keeps you connected to your own sexuality and helps you understand how your body likes to be touched, caressed and pleasured.

4. Change Your Diet

Some foods are aphrodisiacs. Foods like bananas, peanut butter and honey contain vitamin B, which helps to give your libido a natural boost. Celery can also help get you going, as it contains androsterone, a hormone said to aid increase female desire. There are a number of other natural libido boosting foods that can awaken desire.

5. Pamper Yourself

How about treating yourself with a long, warm bubble bath? Feel free to fill the bathtub with warm, bubbly water, surrounded by few of your favourite scented candles. Slipping into the hot water will help your tension melt away. For many women, a lack of cleanliness can also be a serious roadblock to sexiness. Spending a few minutes in a warm shower with some sweet-smelling soaps can help relieve stress for intimacy.

6. Wear Sexy to Feel Sexy

Lace, silk, plain cotton — whatever makes you feel sexy, put it on. Wear it under your clothes all day or slip into it when you get home from work. Having a go-to set of lingerie that makes you feel good will help get you in the mood when you wear it.

7. Relax Yourself

Do whatever you need to take your mind off any worries and relax your mind. Whether it is having some 'me-time,' have a long sleep, lotion yourself, listen to music, speaking to friends, eating some chocolate, going to the gym, take a spa break with a sensual massage, or going on vacation, do whatever you need to do to leave your worries aside and concentrate on enjoying pleasure. Relaxation is crucial to kunyaza as one Rwandan lady says;

> It all starts with foreplay between a man and wife. You touch and caress each other... it's an exchange...the woman must feel relaxed.

8. Non-Sexual Intimacy

Explore other forms of intimacy such as holding hands, talking to each other, cuddling, and touching each other in a non-sexual way. Talking with your partner can help rekindle your interest in sex. Feeling as if you are not being heard is a barrier to sex for many women, so it is important to make sure both you and your partner feel respected, desired and important. Take your time to actively listen to one another. "A lot of couples don't communicate and end up avoiding sex," says Cynthia Graham, professor of sexual and reproductive health. Open and frank communication about sex can help increase female desire, sexual therapists say.

9. Remind Yourself

Take time to remind yourself of passionate encounters you have had. When you have felt sensual and desirable. Fantasise about what you want to do to your partner and what you would like them to do to you. The female libido tends to decrease when women are in a stable long-term relationship. Therefore, it is important to spice up your relationship to keep the passion alive. There is biological evidence that novel experiences cause the release of dopamine and serotonin (pleasure hormone) in the brain.

10. Read Erotica

Erotica is known arouse women, and it's even sexier when you read romantic love scenes thinking about your lover. Lay back, relax and lose yourself in the throes of a blood-pressure-rising romance novel to awaken your hidden desires. Just reading about a passionate love scene can get you mentally and physically turned on.

Tips for Men to Help Her Get in The Mood

To help your lady get in the mood you should get rid of distractions, use soft gentle lighting to help her relax, and create a soft and sensual musical playlist for you both to enjoy. Also take care of your grooming and hygiene needs such as trimming your fingernails, clean your private parts, bathe thoroughly and use perfume to arouse her desire.

In addition, making your woman feel special is extremely important and cannot be overemphasized. You can do this by complimenting her, being attentive to her needs and giving her a long warm hug. Hugging produces oxytocin (love hormone) which lowers stress levels and will give her more energy and happiness. Making her feel desired and letting her know that she is irresistible will also help arouse her desires.

Real mastery in learning how to get your lady in the mood comes from how well you can build trust, be non-judgmental, and be her guiding masculine energy without being forceful. Trust is extremely important when it comes to female sexual arousal. The more a woman trusts her partner, the more confident she will be and let go of her inhibitions and enjoy pleasure. Trust can also help your lady overcome sexual trauma.

Helping Your Lady Overcome Sexual Trauma

Sexual trauma is unfortunately far from an isolated issue. Research shows that one in three women have experienced physical and/or sexual violence. Sexual violence is more common than many people think. Sexual violence is unwanted sexual attention including; sexual assault, rape and sexual abuse. Victims of sexual abuse are likely to develop post-traumatic stress disorder (PTSD). PTSD is an anxiety disorder caused by very stressful, frightening or distressing events.

Women with sex-related PTSD can affect their ability to sexually 'let go' and achieve climax. However, a woman's lover can play a key role with her sexual healing. Women are incredibly resilient, and many are able to recover from the trauma completely with no long term or ongoing difficulties. If you're a man whose lover was sexually assaulted, you can support her recovery process by doing the following;

- You can't heal her or "make" her enjoy sex. She has to heal herself and rediscover erotic pleasure for herself. Your role is to offer emotional support, asking how she feels, and listening to her.

- Go slow. Everything should go at her own pace. Understand that she may need to be in control of sex.

- Whilst making love, check in frequently. Ask, "Is this okay?" "Do you want me to continue?"

- Explore nonsexual sensuality i.e. cuddling, touching, sensual massage, and bathing together. Avoid touching her genitalia. Not every touch should lead to sex.

- Patience, patience, patience! Remember her pleasure is your priority.

Chapter 3: Labia Pulling, FGM and Kunyaza

"Pull your lips and you'll feel that things will be sweeter than they are now."
- Betty Nalongo, Ugandan sex educator

Women all over the world choose to alter their genitalia for various reasons. While some women in the West use weights from sex shops to elongate their genitalia or undergo expensive surgeries to 'beautify' their genitalia by labia reduction, some women in East Africa partake in an ancient practice to manually elongate their labia. Referred to as *gukuna* in Rwanda and *okukyalira ensiko* in Uganda, girls pull their labia in preparation for marital life. Labia pulling is said to help women expel copious fluid emissions during sexual stimulation. Some African researchers believe that labia pulling helps a woman ejaculate and it can enhance pleasure. Other researchers in the West claim that labia pulling is "an abusive practice violating humans rights." This chapter explores whether the controversial practice of labia pulling is a form of female genital mutilation (FGM), why women pull their labia, and whether the practice enhances female pleasure.

What is Labia Pulling?

Labia pulling, also known as labia stretching, labia elongation, and labia minora elongation (LME), is a cultural practice in which the inner vaginal lips are stretched and pulled to elongate the labia minora. The controversial practice is commonly practised in parts of East and Central Africa and is said to increase male and female pleasure during heterosexual encounters.[29] The World Health Organisation (WHO) initially classified labia pulling as a form of female genital mutilation (FGM), until it was challenged and then reclassified as female genital modification. Many Westerners still consider labia pulling to be a form of FGM, especially when performed on a girl. A study concluded that it is more appropriate to describe the Rwandan vaginal practice of labia pulling as a form of female genital modification rather than FGM.

---

[29] Labia pulling is not a new practice nor is it only practised in East and Central Africa; there were recorded sightings of southern African women with elongated labia in the eighteen century. The most famous in the West being Sarah 'Saartjie' Baartman (The Hottentot Venus) from South Africa. Baartman was brought over to Europe in 1810 and was paraded in a cage in Piccadilly Circus, London and later on in Paris to excited onlookers who wanted to see her "gigantic" buttocks and "excessively large" genitalia.

How Do Women Elongate Their Labia?

Traditionally girls elongate their labia with the aid of a ssenga. They use three fingers to pull each of the lips downwards for several weeks. Those past their teenage years have to do it for over a month. Some describe the pulling of the labia is "like milking a cow." The process is aided by traditional herbs supplied by ssengas. Once the labia minora attains their required length, neither too long nor too short, the girls/women are advised to revisit the ssenga for maintenance of the vulval appearance.

A Ugandan woman explains,

> When pulling you press your middle finger (inside the vagina). Then you pull your lips or vagina and measure them with your middle finger. You keep pulling until they are as long as your middle finger. You continue to pull and measure them with your finger until you've reached the right length.

Why Do Women Elongate Their Labia?

Sexual practices vary from culture to culture, and even from tribe to tribe. The practice of labia elongation in some African cultures is thought to help a woman get married. Others state that it is done to enhance the husband's sexual pleasure, and others say that women elongate their labia to enhance pleasure for themselves. It is also believed to help women ejaculate.

Women in diverse cultures have always altered or otherwise transformed their bodies in order to fit their cultural norms. One of the ways that East African women alter their bodies is through a routine of elongating the labia. In the Buganda tribe of Uganda, it is common for women to elongate their labia prior to marriage, as Ugandan men are said to prefer a woman with large labia. Some Ugandan women report that they elongate their labia as it is a tradition and they believe it makes their genitalia more beautiful. Labia elongation is also said to be practised to prevent a man from being unfaithful, as one Kenyan woman said,

> You have to take care of your vagina, otherwise your man doesn't feel anything. Then they will go from one woman to the next. But if you take good care of yourself, he will long for you. He will only think of you.

Labia Pulling (*Gukuna*) in Rwanda

Gukuna is an ancient Rwandan custom where the labia minora are gently pulled or stretched so that they become elongated. It helps to heighten a woman's sexual sensitivity according to tradition. Girls practise gukuna from a young age. It is said that gukuna helps a woman to kunyara (ejaculate) during the practice of kunyaza. Nowadays, the gukuna custom like the kunyaza sexual practice is no longer widely practised in Rwanda, as more urban Rwandans dismiss the traditions as backward practices reserved for rural dwellers. Some Rwandan Christians consider it to be a sin.

Gukuna was originally practised so the elongated skin could help protect and keep a woman's vagina clean. However, when it was discovered that these women were also experiencing heightened sexual sensitivity and were more likely to produce ejaculatory 'water,' it became a customary practice in Rwanda. "Thirty years ago it was like an order," explains Vestine Dusabe. "Every woman that got married had to have gukuna." She adds, "in the old days girls would do it to each other. But now we're concerned this will arouse lesbian feelings, so we teach them to do it individually."

Dusabe admits that she performed gukuna on her two daughters when they were ten years old as she does not want the Rwandan tradition to disappear. A frequent visit to schools, Dusabe informs young girls to pull their lips daily to prepare them for marriage. In Rwanda, a woman with large genital lips is highly sought after. Men frustrated by their wives' lack of gukuna are among Dusabe's most frequent callers to her radio show.

For gukuna advocates, a woman performing pulling is not an automatic pass to induce female ejaculation. A man must also do his part. This means making the woman feel comfortable, engaging in foreplay and demonstrating sound kunyaza technique. Even then, it's not guaranteed. "It depends on your feeling, and your connection," explains a Rwandan woman.

Labia Pulling (*Okukyalira Ensiko*) in Uganda

In western Uganda, women of the Bahima clan used to make their labia minora long enough to cover the vaginal opening. Known as *okukyalira ensiko* (visiting the bush), this rite is traditionally performed in a clearing among bushes where herbs (such as *mukasa, entengotengo, oluwoko*) used for the procedure were found. Pubescent girls would 'visit the bush' for a few hours every day over a period of about two weeks. The ssenga would persuade them to comply by advising them that if they did not, no man would ever ask for their hand in marriage. When a Ugandan man discovered that his bride had not 'visited the bush' he would send her back to her parents for the ssenga to fulfil her duty.[30] Dr. James Sengendo and Dr. Emmanuel Sekatawa from Kampala Uganda explains;

> A [Muganda] woman who did not elongate the labia minora is traditionally despised and regarded as having a pit. If a bride was found not to have elongated her labia minora, she would be returned to her parents with disgrace.[31]

In the documentary, *The Sunny Side of Sex in Uganda*, the film's director, Sunny Bergman, meets a group of Ugandan women to discuss labia pulling in her hometown of Amsterdam, the Netherlands. The women were not ashamed or shy to talk about sex. Intrigued, Bergman travelled to Uganda to better understand these women who are proud of their large genitalia. While in Uganda, Bergman was introduced to the practice of labia pulling, where it was believed that the practice enhances women's own pleasure, not necessarily that of their men.

Bergman posed one lady the question, "don't you get aroused in the process?" "No," she was informed. "You have to think of it as a service you do for a friend, there is nothing sexual about it. I didn't think of it as lesbian," said a Ugandan ssenga who performs labia pulling on women. There was no shame attached to a large genitalia amongst Ugandan women. In fact, in Uganda, long protruding lips are praiseworthy. In the West, small tucked lips are desired which women obtain by way of labiaplasty cosmetic surgery.

Labiaplasty is a surgical procedure to reduce or reshape the labia minora (inner lips). The procedure is very popular amongst women in the West. It is also called "labia minora reduction," "labia reduction," or "inner lip reduction." The most common reason for the surgery is for aesthetic purposes.[32] A popular labiaplasty procedure is known as *The Barbie*, which involves removing the entire labia minora to give a Barbie-doll like look of a

---

[30] Jolly, S., *et al.*, *Women, Sexuality and the Political Power of Pleasure*
[31] Sengendo, J., and Sekatawa, E., 'A Cultural Approach to HIV/AIDS Prevention and Care'
[32] Another vaginal cosmetic surgery procedure is vaginoplasty, a surgical procedure to 'tighten' the vagina.

smooth genitalia. Labiaplasty is also known as 'designer vagina' surgery in some countries in the Western world.

Ironically, whilst many white women in America flock to cosmetic surgeons to perform labiaplasty in quest for the "perfect vagina," many black women in Africa embrace their large labia and even try to extend it by labia pulling. In an exchange with a Ugandan woman, Dutch director Sunny Bergman informed a Ugandan lady who had performed labia pulling, that the Dutch call a woman's labia, "shame lips." In which the Ugandan lady replied,

> Why? How can you be ashamed of your own body? You should be proud of what you have, [and] the way you are as a woman.

Bergman's findings challenge many of the preconceived ideas about female sexuality in Africa, as well as the notion that Western ideas about female sexuality is more sophisticated compared to 'less developed' countries. For all the wealth and perceived progressive culture in the West, there is still a lot that the Western world can learn from African women in traditional cultures about female sexuality.[33]

Is Labia Pulling a Form of Female Genital Mutilation (FGM)?

Female genital mutilation (FGM) also called, female genital cutting, is a practice that has been documented among peoples in certain parts of the world, regardless of religious belief or ethnic background. Sometimes FGM is inaccurately referred to as female circumcision.

FGM includes procedures and practices meant to intentionally injure or alter the female genital organs for non-medical reasons, according to the World Health Organisation (WHO). The WHO initially deemed the labia pulling practice as a form of FGM. However after a study by Marian Koster and Lisa Price, it was reclassified as 'female genital modification' in 2008. According to WHO, FGM is classified into 4 types;

- **Type 1:** Clitoridectomy - The partial or total removal of the clitoris, and in some cases, only the prepuce (clitoris hood).

---

[88] Koster, M., and Price, L., 'Rwandan Female Genital Modification: Elongation of the Labia minora and the Use of Local Botanical Species,' pp. 191-204

- **Type 2:** Excision – The partial or total removal of the clitoris and the labia minora (inner lips), with or without excision of the labia majora (outer lips). The remaining skin may be stitched together.

- **Type 3:** Infibulation – The removal of all or part of the clitoris and the labia minora and labia majora. The raw skin is then stitched together, leaving a tiny opening for urination and menstruation. The tiny opening reopens during childbirth and is then re-stitched.

- **Type 4:** Other – This includes all other harmful procedures to the female genitalia for non-medical purposes, e.g. pricking, piercing, incising, scraping and cauterizing the genital area.

Dr. Sylvia Tamale mounts a strong defence for labia pulling and castigates "Western bigots for displaying their usual double-standards in fighting this African tradition." In her paper, *Eroticism, Sensuality and "Women's Secrets" among the Baganda: A Critical Analysis,* Tamale writes:

> Classifying it (Okukyalira ensiko) and condemning it as type-IV female genital mutilation, the WHO lumps this procedure together with FGM procedures that pose health hazards to women. It completely disregards the ways in which this practice, encoded within the ssenga institution, has enhanced sexual pleasure for women, and expanded their perceptions of themselves as active sexual beings.

> Interestingly, harmful cosmetic procedures (such as clitoral piercing) sometimes performed in Western countries are not listed under type-IV FGM. Through such discourse, this global health body writes this African practice of sexual enhancement into the broad negative rubric of harmful cultural practices that violate the rights of women and children.

Does FGM Affect Orgasms?

The severity of the FGM procedure depends on differences in locale, educational attainment, and socioeconomic status rather than religious affiliation or ethnic origin. Depending on the type of genital cutting and the parts that are injured or removed, women can have a variety of experiences in their sex life, including orgasm.[34] Dr. Bizimana said,

---

[34] Komisaruk B., *et al., The Orgasm Answer Guide,* p. 114

In most circumstances, only a small part of the female clitoris is excised (after FGM). The internal part is preserved, as well as the urinary meatus, which is a very erogenous zone. So these women could be satisfied. We have the tendency of thinking that they cannot be satisfied sexually, whereas they can. I have interviewed excised women who have confirmed that the kunyaza method works for them.

Does Labia Pulling Enhance Pleasure?

Large labia are beneficial to a woman's pleasure according to a number of ssengas such as Betty Katana Nalongo. Labia elongation is supposed to make orgasm easier to achieve because when the vaginal lips are long they are easier to grab and play with during foreplay. They cover the penis and cause more friction during intercourse. Ugandan journalist Yahya Sseremba, passionately argues why he believes labia pulling enhances sexual pleasure, for both women and men. In his article 'Okukyalira Ensiko: the Buganda way of enhancing sexual pleasure,' Sseremba writes

> During intercourse, these elongated lips tickle the penis as it gets in and gently squeezes it as it pulls out. To men, this is a blissful spice up. To women, it evokes heavenly feelings as the penis titillates the sensitive lips during inward and outward movements. This titillation stimulates the woman to reach orgasm or even multiple orgasms faster, a level of excitement that some women hardly experience because of the inexperience of their spouses.

Sseremba reports that women of the Bahima clan in western Uganda used to elongate their labia to cover their vaginal opening to raise barricades for rapists. However, in the Buganda tribe the elongation of the inner labia has become a salient feature with which women distinguish themselves from women of other tribes. For women of the Buganda tribe, long lips builds confidence and self-esteem. It's highly arousing for men and considered an aesthetic for women.

The most often stated benefit for *okukyalira ensiko* (labia pulling) is to keep the vagina warm, Sseremba writes. Long inner lips stretching to the opening of the vagina, experts say, serve as "a blanket that that keeps the warmth of the sexual organ intact." One ssenga described the labia minora as "doors that close" the vagina and keep its temperature warm at enjoyable levels.

A stern critic of Western cultural imperialism, Sseremba defends the Ugandan practice of labia pulling and kachabali to enhance sexual pleasure. The journalist criticises "puritanical young" Muslims in Uganda who try to eradicate the country's sexual practices. According to Sseremba, the religion of Islam is not against cultural practices such as labia pulling as it does not contradict the religion's teachings. Religion may overlap with culture but it is not synonymous with it. While the Islamic religion restricts some forms of sexuality i.e. pre-marital and extra-marital relations, the practice of labia pulling and kachabali, is not prohibited, according to Sseremba. Rather he urges Ugandan Muslims to be embrace their cultural heritage which promotes female sexual pleasure within the confines of a marital relationship.

For Sseremba, many "ignorant" Europeans and Americans demonise African cultural traditions and lack respect of the continent's values, morals and customs. Although the journalist is not from the Buganda tribe where labia pulling is practised, he wants African cultures and traditions to be respected by those outside the country. Sseremba says,

> Far from promoting promiscuity as one ignorant European writer claims, the tradition prepares girls for what society considers the most enjoyable and most pleasurable form of lovemaking.

> In fact, one of Kampala's leading ssenga told me that European women have started coming to her to have their labia minora elongated. The people of the West would certainly learn a lot from Africa if they overcame their bigotry.

Chapter 4: The Clitoris, Clitoral Stimulation and Kunyaza

The clitoris is the only organ in the human body with the sole purpose of providing pleasure. It's a female sex organ which contains more erogenous nerve endings than any other organ in the female body. In fact, most women experience orgasm by clitoral stimulation. This amazing, mysterious organ is essential for the practice of kunyaza. Clitoral stimulation, referred to as *rugongo*, in Rwanda, is indispensable for inducing an intense orgasm accompanied with a gush of erotic fluid. This chapter provides an introduction to the female genitalia, the clitoris (K-Spot), and female masturbation techniques.

The Female Genitalia

The external female reproductive structure is referred to collectively as the vulva. The mons pubis is a pad of fat that is located at the anterior, over the pubic bone. The labia majora (larger lips) are folds of hair-covered skin that begin just posterior to the mons pubis. The thinner and more pigmented labia minora (smaller lips) extend medial to the labia majora. Although they naturally vary in shape and size from woman to woman, the labia minora serve to protect the female urethra and the entrance to the female reproductive tract.

The larger anterior portions of the labia minora come together to encircle the clitoris glans, an organ that originates from the same cells as the glans penis and has abundant nerves that make it important in sexual sensation and orgasm. The hymen is a thin membrane that sometimes partially covers the entrance to the vagina. The vagina (vaginal opening) is located between the opening of the urethra and the anus. It is flanked by outlets to the Bartholin's glands (or greater vestibular glands).

Get to Know Your Lady Parts

Sex educators encourage women to get to know their bodies and explore what arouses them in order to be able to inform their male partners what pleases them in the bedroom. Given the fact that most women do not frequently experience orgasm, it is incumbent on them and their partners to learn about her body, and her most responsive erogenous zones.

Sex therapist Dr Andrea Pennington and author of *The Orgasm Prescription For Women*, said: "Women often feel very uncomfortable with their bodies." A survey for cancer charity *The Eve Appeal*, found just one in five men thought his partner's lady garden was attractive and most did not know the difference between the vagina and vulva. Many people believe that the vulva - the external female sexual organs comprising of the labia and clitoris among other parts - is in fact the vagina. CEO of The Eve Appeal Athena Lamnisos said;

> Body confidence is important, but body knowledge is absolutely vital, and our research has shown that women don't know their vaginas from their vulvas. The more knowledge a woman has about her body, the more likely she will know what turns her on.

Below is the external and internal anterolateral view of the vulva;

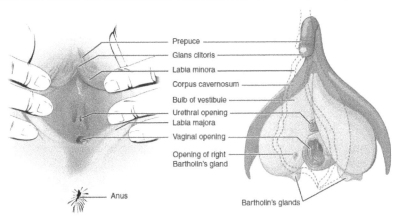

The Clitoris and the K-Spot

The clitoris is the hub of female pleasure. It is the most sensitive erogenous zone of the female body.[35] The clitoris has over 8,000 nerve endings, which is nearly twice the amount found in the penis. Reportedly the most intense

---

[35] Erogenous zones are areas of the body that elicit a sexual response when stimulated. By stimulating an erogenous zone, a sexual physiological response can occur followed by an orgasm. Erogenous zones can include the genitalia, breasts or nape.

part of the clitoris glans is on the top left-hand side. For some women the clitoris will become very sensitive especially when a woman is fully aroused or just after climax. The usage of the word 'clitoris' in this book refers to the clitoris glans or glans clitoris, unless otherwise stated.

Etymology

The word 'clitoris' has its origin in Ancient Greek, *kleitoris*, likely from the verb *kleiein*, "to shut," in reference to it being covered by the labia minora. The related Greek noun *kleis* has a secondary meaning "a key, a latch or hook (to close the door)," indicating that the ancient anatomists considered "the clitoris is the key to female sexuality."

Clitoris is defined in the Oxford dictionary as "a small, sensitive, erectile part of the female genitals at the anterior end of the vulva." In reality the clitoris structure is larger than this definition and what many people think. The clitoris is like an iceberg. Most of its structure sits inside a woman's body. An average clitoris is approximately 10 centimetres long. The clitoris is made of up the external (visible) and internal (non-visible) clitoris.

Structure of Clitoris and Penis

The clitoris and penis are similar in structure. In fact, they actually originate from the same development tissue. Many of the parts of the clitoris are similar to that of the penis, but differ in shape and size, and are located in different places. The overall shape of the clitoris resembles a thick wishbone, consisting of the visible clitoris glans in the midline, the clitoral body, corpus cavernosum, and two branches; the vestibular bulbs and the crura ('legs'). The clitoris is not just the part of the vulva that looks like a small pea. Both the bulbs and legs of the clitoris are erectile tissues that can become rigid when aroused. The deep components of the clitoris can develop an erection by becoming engorged with blood, similar to what happens in a penis.

The corpus cavernosum of the clitoris is one of a pair of sponge-like regions of erectile tissue which form the bulk of the clitoris. The corpus cavernosum contain most of the blood in the clitoris during clitoral erection. The corpus cavernosum of the clitoris is homologous to the corpus cavernosum penis in males.

External Parts of the Clitoris

The glans clitoris is the name of the part that most people call the 'clitoris.' It is the external part of the clitoris, about the size of a pea, and is located above the urethra. Because the glans is the most highly innervated area of the clitoris, it's extremely sensitive to touch. The glans does not contain erectile (expandable) tissue, so it does not swell or grow during the female sexual response. The function of the clitoris glans is to detect sensation and stimulation.

Just above or on top of the clitoris glans is the clitoral hood (prepuce), which is formed by the two sides of the connecting labia minora. Clitoral hoods (prepuce) can vary in size and degree of coverage from woman to woman. The clitoral hood covers the external shaft of the clitoris, and is homologous with the foreskin in the male genitalia. The prepuce is formed by the two sides of the connecting labia minora. During sexual excitement, the prepuce swells slightly, so that the clitoris glans becomes less visible.

Internal Parts of the Clitoris

Beneath the clitoris glans, the rest of the clitoris extends deep into the body and is attached by supporting connective tissues to the pubic bone, mons pubis, labia urethra, and vagina. The majority of the clitoris is not visible to the human eye when looking at the vulva. Connected to the clitoris glans is the body of the clitoris. The clitoral body projects upwards into the pelvis, and attaches via ligaments to the pubic bone.

From the clitoris body (located in front of the urethra), the clitoris splits in half to form the paired crura ('legs'), and vestibular bulbs. These bulbs extend through and behind the labia, passing by the urethra, vaginal canal and towards the anus.

The bulbs and crura contain erectile tissue that swells with blood during female sexual arousal. By swelling on either side of the vaginal canal, they increase lubrication in the vagina, while increasing sexual stimulation and sensation. This expansion to clitoral tissue can also cause pressure to be applied to the anterior of the vaginal canal.

The K-Spot

For the purpose of this book, the K-Spot refers to the entire clitoris structure which resembles the letter 'K.' The K-Spot is both the internal and external parts of the clitoris.

The anatomy and function of the clitoris is a hotly debated topic, as is another erogenous area which is said to give women incredible pleasure – the G-Spot. Described by some as the female prostate, the G-Spot has been well-researched in numerous studies, but its existence remains contested. Some researchers claim that stimulation of the G-Spot area (front anterior vaginal wall) induces female ejaculation (and squirting). Other researchers suggest that the G-Spot is not an actual physical anatomy, but is instead the area where the sides of the vestibular bulbs of the clitoris make contact with the anterior wall of the vagina (the 'clitoral network'). This means that the G-Spot is actually the clitoris as its part of the clitoral network.

The controversial G-Spot was named after German gynaecologist Ernst Gräfenberg in 1982, after he 'discovered' the erotic area in 1950. As Rwandans and other Africans have spoken about the clitoral area for centuries, I want to pay homage to them by naming the area as the K-Spot, after the 'k-shaped structure' clitoral network and the kunyaza technique which focuses on clitoral stimulation. Below is an illustration of the anatomy of the clitoris (internal and external parts), also known as the K-Spot;

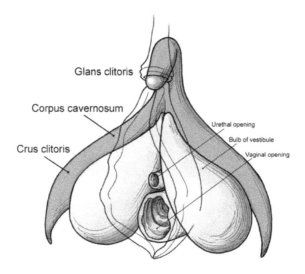

Friction around the clitoral area sends nerve impulses up the dorsal nerve of the clitoris, and as a consequence to the pudendal nerve, and then the spinal cord and the brain. Provided that a woman is relaxed and in the mood for sexual stimulation, these nerve signals will cause her to become highly aroused and may eventually lead to climax. Sexual intercourse does not generally involve the direct stimulation of the clitoris, except in certain sex positions, such as the coitally adjusted technique (CAT) position. Kunyaza provides indirect and direct stimulation of the K-Spot with the pressing, stroking and tapping of the penis on the labia and clitoris glans.

Misconceptions About The Female Genitalia

The female genitalia comes in different shapes and sizes. Every woman has a unique looking vulva, vagina and labia. Each woman's genitalia varies in terms of tightness, depth, wetness, warmth, and appearance. Not all vaginas are the same, just like how not all women are the same. Mainstream media and pornography has influenced many people's perception of a woman's private parts and led to some misconceptions about the female genitalia and clitoris. Some of these are related below;

1. "The clitoris is small"

The clitoris may look like a small pea, but it is more like an iceberg. The actual clitoris is much larger than just the visible portion of the glans. On average, the clitoris is eleven centimetres long. The actual clitoris is more like the penis, they both have a prepuce (foreskin), glans, and erectile tissue.

2. "The vagina is the same as the vulva"

The vagina is not the same as the vulva. The vagina is a tube of muscle that joins the cervix and the vaginal opening; the vulva is the exterior genitalia.

3. "Vaginas smell bad"

Certified sexual health educator Angelica Lindsey-Ali informs,

> We have been fooled into believing that vaginas inherently emit a 'bad' smell. This is partially due to social programming and the fact that, when unhealthy, the vagina can produce an off-putting odour. However, a healthy vagina is supposed to smell like...you. A clean well-cared for female sex organ has a smell which is neither pungent nor sweet. It has a distinct scent which is found to be erotically pleasing to men. You are not a flower and are not meant to smell like one.

> Stop using douches and vaginal washes which contain unhealthy chemicals that interfere with the healthy flora and fauna of your vagina. Make sure that you clean your external genitalia properly. Don't use harsh soaps which can cause irritation. Drink lots of water. Eat healthy foods. Incorporate foods with healthy bacteria (probiotics). Don't wear tight fitting clothing that can suffocate your vagina.

> Get comfortable with your natural scent. It's there for a reason. But be aware if something smells 'off'. If you smell of fish, bread, or

mildew below, that is a sure sign of infection. Seek medical help from a trusted gynaecologist.

4. "The bigger the penis, the stronger the woman's pleasure"

Most women do not experience orgasm from intercourse alone, irrespective of penis size. It's the clitoris not the vagina which is key to female pleasure. The average erect penis ranges between 4 to 7 inches in length and 3 to 4 inches in circumference. A micro (small) penis is 2.8 inches or shorter when erect, and a macrophallus (abnormally large penis) is 8 inches or longer when erect. The average vaginal cavity is 4 to 6 inches in depth. Therefore, an average size penis is more than capable of providing the average woman sufficient pleasure during intercourse. Penis size does not necessarily provide increased pleasure as the vaginal cavity does not have many nerve endings like the clitoris, which has 8,000 approximately.

5. "Vaginas are unclean"

The vagina is a self-cleaning organ. It keeps itself safe and hygienic with secretions. A truly amazing organ, it is lined with a mucous membrane that protects against infection, as well as a complex mix of bacteria. Together, they keep the vagina healthy.

6. "The vulva is ugly"

Every vulva is different and special. Vulvas do not look the same. Every woman has a unique looking vulva and labia size. The average length of the labia minora is less than one inch long. Less than five percent of women have labia longer than two inches. Some lips hang down. Some are tucked up neatly inside. Some are long. Some are short. Some are even. Some aren't. All are beautifully created by God.

Clitoral Stimulation to Enhance Her Pleasure

The finger, the penis and the tongue are each effective love instruments in their own right to stimulate the clitoris. Some women prefer manual stimulation with the fingers, other prefer the delicate touch of the tongue, and others prefer the firmness of an erect penis to engorge the clitoris and heighten arousal, prior to intercourse. Whatever a woman desires, her male sexual partner should use the appropriate love instrument to pleasure her.

The Golden Trio

According to a US study, women are more likely to orgasm if a sexual encounter includes deep kissing, manual genital stimulation, and/or oral sex (known as the 'golden trio') in addition to vaginal intercourse. Previous studies have shown that there is a notable gap between heterosexual men and heterosexual women in orgasm frequency during sex. The American researchers considered the 'sociocultural and evolutionary explanations' for the orgasm gap between men and women.

Based on the responses from 52,588 male and female participants aged between 18 and 65 years, who answered questions about their sex lives, the study found that 95% of heterosexual men usually-always orgasm when sexually intimate, compared with 65% of heterosexual women. However, when a sexual encounter includes a combination of; deep kissing, genital (clitoral) stimulation, and/or oral stimulation, 80% of women experience an orgasm. The study underlines the importance of clitoral stimulation in achieving climax. Co-author of the study, Elisabeth Lloyd, said,

> About 30% of men actually think that intercourse is the best way for women have orgasm, and that is sort of a tragic figure because it couldn't be more incorrect. To say that there needs to be some education I think is an understatement.

Published in the *Archives of Sexual Behavior*, the American scientists also found that women who do orgasm with their partners are more likely to feel satisfied with their relationship as a whole. Whilst the 'golden trio' is said to significantly increase the likelihood of a woman experiencing an orgasm with a male partner the authors admit that there is no 'one size fits all' approach to orgasming.[36]

Triggering Female Orgasm in 5 Minutes with Kunyaza

To trigger the female orgasm, intense stimulation of the 'magic bean' (clitoris) with the male member is recommended. Rwandan sex researcher Dr. Bizimana claimed that women are capable of climaxing within five minutes of kunyaza stimulation;

---

[36] Frederick, D., *et al,* 'Differences in Orgasm Frequency Among Gay, Lesbian, Bisexual, and Heterosexual Men and Women in a U.S. National Sample,' pp. 273-288

When performed properly, kunyaza is a highly effective technique, whereby a woman can achieve an orgasm within 3 to 5 minutes.

Clitoral stimulation, referred to as *rugongo*, in Rwanda and Burundi, is indispensable for inducing the female orgasm. When asked to explain the meaning of kunyaza, Rwandese and Burundians answered that it consists of stroking or striking the *rugongo*. 'Hitting the bean' is fundamental to causing climax in women, ssengas teach. This has also been confirmed by modern scientific studies, which have proved that clitoral stimulation is arguably the most effective stimulation method to trigger the female orgasm.

Female Masturbation and Clitoral Stimulation Techniques

Female masturbation is the self-stimulation of the sexual organs, most often to the point of climax. Also referred to as self-pleasure, masturbation for women is a safe and natural way to feel good, discover what turns them on and release built-up sexual tension. A woman can learn a great deal about her sexual response through masturbation, which she can then pass on to her male partner to improve their love life.

Some ssengas encourage women to explore their sexuality by way of masturbation to understand what arouses them before engaging in kunyaza with a male partner. In addition, Western sex researchers encourage women to self-pleasure to understand their bodies and erogenous zones. A British study found that women who had recently masturbated were more likely to report a higher interest in sex, while the opposite was true for men. This finding reflects the tendency among women to consider masturbation as part of a "broader repertoire of sexual fulfilment," said the study's authors, rather than a substitute for partnered sex.[37] Some research suggests that female masturbation can help boost self-awareness, social competence, body esteem and improve intimacy in long-term relationships. "One reason women lack interest in sex is that sex isn't always very good with a partner," says Dr. Cynthia Graham. She adds,

> Masturbation can help women learn things they can then teach their partners about how to pleasure them.

---

[37] Graham, C., Mercer, C., Tanton, C., *et al.* 'What factors are associated with reporting lacking interest in sex and how do these vary by gender? Findings from the third British national survey of sexual attitudes and lifestyles.'

In the context of the kunyaza tradition, the purpose of female masturbation is for a woman to understand her sexuality better in order to inform her male partner how to arouse her. Ugandan ssenga Betty Nalongo advises,

> When you go to your bed and lie on your back, use your (index) finger to touch the bean (clitoris) yourself.
> And do it like this, squeeze it like this (firmly pressing finger on the clitoris).
> You will feel (sensations) and you should close your eyes and go on until you reach orgasm.
> It is because of this bean (clitoris). Everything is in that bean!

Based on scientific research, the OMGYES sex educational website provides various masturbation techniques.[38] The website aims to "educate women how to have better, more enjoyable orgasms." Backed up by research of the testimonies of everyday women, the study summarised twelve female masturbation techniques which a woman or her partner can practise to help her reach the big O! These are presented below;

1. **Accenting** involves giving the clitoris more or less attention on specific parts of each repeated motion. Pleasure isn't symmetrical. About one in eight women prefer more attention on the right side of the vulva, while the same number prefer more on the left. Experiment with putting more pressure on each side to see if you prefer one or the other.

2. **Edging** involves paying attrition to your level of arousal, and developing your ability to know when you are getting close to orgasm. When you approach orgasm, you tone down stimulation and you practice 'riding that edge' – staying just under the threshold of orgasm. Repeatedly coming close to an orgasm—but preventing it before it happens—builds longer, more intense orgasms for most women. To intensify the orgasm you can build up anticipation; by completely stopping all touch right before orgasm and resuming once the feeling subsides, touching somewhere else to distract your body temporarily, or continuously switching between the kind of touch that brings you to orgasm and other, less intense touches.

---

[38] OMGYES is a research-based sex-ed website about women's pleasure. The site includes a video library of instructional videos on masturbation techniques for women. OMGYES's founders in partnership with researchers at Indiana University and The Kinsey Institute, conducted extensive interviews with 2,000 women in the United States between the ages of 18 and 95 to help women have better orgasms.

3. **Hinting** involves building anticipation by repeatedly approaching sensitive areas but only occasionally indulging them with attention, often used as a foreplay technique. To try it, stimulate everything except the clitoris, including the inner thighs and labia, using a light touch.

4. **Multiples** simply refers to overcoming the sensitivity after orgasm to rebuild to additional orgasms after the first. 47% of women in the OMGYES study reported to having multiple orgasms, and five out of six of them said they achieved a second orgasm with a different set of techniques than what worked for the first.

5. **Consistency** involves simply keeping the motion constant to build up pleasure and intensify orgasm.

6. **Orbiting** is when the clitoris is stimulated with some kind of continuous circular motion, 78.1% of women in the study prefer this technique. Orgasm through orbiting often involves constant stimulation with continuous motions around the clitoris in circles, ovals, or figure eights.

7. **Surprise** refers to using varying motions to keep the body guessing. It could involve interchanging basic techniques like Rhythm, Hinting, Edging, and Accenting. One way to enhance your pleasure is to keep you on your toes by switching up the rhythm or motion.

8. **Rhythm** refers to the timing pattern of motion, almost like musical rhythm. There are a few different rhythms you or your partner can experiment with when touching your lady parts: taking a break between each motion, skipping every other motion, pausing for varying amounts of time between different motions, doing one motion continuously, and moving very fast like a vibrator.

9. **Layering** involves stimulating the clitoris indirectly, which 66.5% of women enjoy. This could involve stimulating the clitoris by moving the layers of skin around it, or through a thin layer of clothing.

10. **Signalling** is when you give and read signals to improve pleasure and orgasm. Although it's not a physical technique, the study found that 89.3% of women enjoyed it. Signalling to your male partner what you

like is most likely to improve pleasure for women, and, for partners, how to properly read those signals and act on it.

11. **Framing** can have a drastic effect on your pleasure. Women interviewed in the study often said, for example, that thinking about orgasming actually kept them from doing it. For male partners, the keys to helping women reach the finish line is making it clear you enjoy the process, not getting impatient, and making them feel sexy so they're not distracted by self-conscious thoughts.

12. **Staging** is where everything changes moment by moment. When a woman adheres to the sensitivity changes in her body and adjusts them to reach an orgasm. If she needs less stimulation, she backs off, if she needs more, she will step it up.

Sex Toys and Vibrators

The popularity of adult (sex) toys has increased over the past decade. Sex toys and "vibrators can be a wonderful thing because for many women, it's the only way they can have an orgasm," says sex therapist Dr. Lori Buckley. But, she adds, "like ice cream, too much of a good thing isn't always good," as some women can become dependent on vibrators to achieve an orgasm. Some women report that the heavy-usage of sex-toys and watching porn changed their attitudes towards men and sexuality. Others claimed their "sex addiction caused anxiety" and a need to watch more "hardcore and violent" material to experience pleasure.

An over-reliance on vibrators can also be detrimental to relationships, according to some sex educators. Research suggests that some people who frequently masturbate alone report lower levels of sexual satisfaction with a sexual partner. Afterall, men cannot compete with vibrators just like women cannot compete with porn. Similar to pornography, research has found that sex toys can ruin a relationship when self-pleasure becomes more important than mutual pleasure in a relationship. Certified sexual health educator Angelica Lindsey-Ali advises;

> You may also consider easing up on use of the vibrator during sex. Sex toys are a fun way to add variety and spice to the bedroom but when used too often they become a crutch. Try the kunyaza technique and see if that helps.

Chapter 5: The Kunyaza Technique

"A man is not a man, unless he can make his woman water."
– Ali Kakonge Simba, Ugandan sex herbalist

Kunyaza empowers women who frequently ejaculate, awakens hidden sensations of women who rarely ejaculate, and introduces a new possibility of sexual pleasure to women who did not know that they could ejaculate. The technique liberates women to experience the fountain of erotic pleasure. It involves the tapping, rubbing and stroking of the female flower with the penis head to inflame a woman's desire and send her into ecstasy. This chapter presents how to practice kunyaza, non-penetrative and penetrative stimulation techniques and effective sex positions.

How To Practice Kunyaza

Kunyaza is an invitation to rediscover an age-old treasure of intense erotic experiences in an uncomplicated and highly pleasurable way as well as giving give your wife never experienced climaxes before. The male sexual partner is not left out in sharing this joy. Because you are the one who stimulates her with your erect penis. And what the woman experiences will also give you pleasurable sensations. Because what could be better than to bringing your lady to orgasm!

The kunyaza technique involves a combination of non-penetrative (rubbing and tapping) and penetrative (deep thrusting) stimulation of the internal and external female genitalia with the penis to enhance female pleasure and achieve female orgasm accompanied with ejaculation. There are two types of the kunyaza practice, simple and complex, which are described below.

Simple Kunyaza

During the simple practice of kunyaza, the man rhythmically and continuously taps and strikes the clitoris glans with the head of his erect penis (glans penis). The man takes hold of the penis shaft between his index and middle fingers to perform kunyaza, moving in the same motion from top to bottom and vice versa, or from left to right and vice versa. Eventually the man can make circular movements around the clitoris, also working in the same movement clockwise and then counter clockwise.

Alternatively, the man can stimulate the vulva by lightly striking the clitoris glans and labia minora with his penis to increase arousal. Both the glans penis and the penis shaft should be used by pressing firmly against her genitalia. The vulva can also be stimulated with the penis by using a zigzagging motion from the prepuce of the clitoris to the vagina.

It may also be helpful to use saliva or lubricant to moisten her genitalia. A combination of teasing and massaging the vulva, with the aid of lubrication, if required, heightens her arousal.

Complex Kunyaza

During the complex practice of kunyaza, the following is performed under the following steps;

1. Following vaginal lubrication though foreplay, the man introduces her erect penis into the vagina to perform the conventional penile-vaginal-penetration (PVP), in the course of which he moves his penis backward and forward in the vagina;

2. After the penis has become moist enough, he removes it from the vagina and takes it into his hand or between the index and middle finger, as done during simple kunyaza, and then he rhythmically and repeatedly strikes the external surfaces of the labia minora with the penis glans, working in the same movement from top to bottom and vice versa, from left to right and vice versa, or from top to bottom in a zigzagging motion, and back again in a similar manner, with the stimulation of the glans and body of the clitoris;

3. When her genitalia enlarges and labia minora opens due to increased arousal, he performs similar movements in the area of the internal surfaces of the labia minora and the vestibule, including the external urethral opening;

4. This step consists of stimulating, always in the same movement, the clitoris, the vulval vestibule, the labia minora and the vaginal opening. The man proceeds in a manner similar to that described above, by moving from the prepuce of the clitoris to the inferior margin of the vaginal opening;

5. Finally, almost simultaneously the man stimulates all the organs of the vulva (body and glans of the clitoris, vestibule, labia minora, vaginal opening) and the perineum, moving from the beginning of the body of the clitoris to the perineal area and vice versa. This is the most commonly used form.

Following vaginal lubrication through simple and / or complex kunyaza, the man should proceed to penetrative stimulation as he introduces his manhood into the woman's well to engage in PVP.

Non-Penetrative and Penetrative Stimulation

There are two types of stimulation for kunyaza: non-penetrative and penetrative. Non-penetrative stimulation involves the striking, tapping, and rubbing of the clitoris, labia majora and labia minora with the penis. Penetrative stimulation involves the deep and / or shallow thrusts into the vagina with the penis to achieve the outpouring of pleasure. For both forms of stimulation, the man should simultaneously stimulate different female erogenous zones on the vulva and inside the vagina.

Non-penetrative stimulation involves the following;

- First, he should stimulate the labia minora by tapping and rubbing with his penis and then, at a certain level of arousal, he should proceed to stimulate the internal surfaces of the labia minora and the vulval vestibule, including the urinary meatus in the same manner, followed by the stimulation of the clitoris, vulval vestibule, labia minora and the vaginal opening.

- Performing kunyaza, the man rhythmically and firmly strikes the clitoris glans with his erect penis. As the woman becomes more aroused and the vulva starts to swell, he rubs his penis from the top to the bottom of the vulva, then left to right, and then in a zigzagging motion – always returning to strike the clitoris after each rotation.

- As the woman is brought close to orgasm, he simultaneously stimulates the whole vulval area with long strokes of his penis but never penetrating.

80

Penetrative stimulation involves the following;

- As the woman becomes more aroused and lubricated, the man should take his penis in his hand, between the middle and the thumb/index finger and slowly penetrate the vagina with alternating shallow thrusts (*gucuga*) at the vaginal opening, with deep thrusts (*gucumita*) pushing against the cervix while maintaining exaggerated circular movements between the vagina walls in a 'screwing' fashion during penetration.

- Then the man should penetrate slowly and, still holding the penis with his hands, alternate the movements within the vaginal canal. In the first third of the vagina (on average 3 cm deep), the walls are more sensitive. There it is worth rubbing the clitoris well in many senses and rhythms. The intensity of the back and forth increases as she gets aroused or asks.

The man may alternate between non-penetrative and penetrative stimulation whilst performing kunyaza. This involves changing to penetrative (internal) stimulation by removing his penis to slowly thrusting into her vagina before returning to non-penetrative (external) stimulation of the vulva with the practise of simple and / or complex kunyaza.

During both non-penetrative and penetrative stimulation, the rhythm and the force of the movements should be slow and gentle, unless the woman requires a faster and firmer pressure to enhance arousal. Some couples also use sex toys on the clitoris during penetrative stimulation to enhance the experience for the woman. It can also help if the man tires.

Importance of Female Participation

Kunyaza involves female participation too. The woman can help with the process by cooperating with her partner continue with the stimuli she wants to receive and the intensity of the rhythm that will be used, as well as by communicating with her partner which parts of her genitalia respond best to the stimuli. Open and honest communication is vital at this stage.

Both partners may also take turns. If the man has difficulties stimulating the vestibule. She can help him by spreading apart the labia minora with her fingers until the whole vestibular area is accessible to the penis. Exposing the vestibule to enable the man to access the woman's most sensitive areas, including the G-Spot. To allow him to comfortably stimulate the area between the labia minora and labia majora, she can also spread them apart with her fingers until the area between them is laid out. Should the man tire during the encounter, the woman can take his penis in her hand and continue to kunyaza until he is ready again.

Men Who Love Female Ejaculation and Kunyaza

Tharcisse, 83, Rwandan farmer says:

> Kunyaza is for the man and for the woman, because there is synchronization.

Sex herbalist Ali Kakonge Simba from Uganda says:

> You're not a man until you've made a woman water!

A Kenyan man says:

> If he's really good, it's going to look like somebody has been taking a shower. But if it doesn't happen the woman might go and find some other man. I had friends who did this if their husband didn't give them water.

A Ugandan man says:

> For sex to be exciting, a woman needs to have long vaginal lips.

Felix, a 68-year-old Rwandan says:

> Sex is for the woman. This is because the man has to please her and put her body in a certain state. Her pleasure is the most important thing.

Manzi, 22, media student, says:

> It is my priority to pleasure the woman. I come after. I enjoy it so much if she releases, the energy she lets off. It's magical. I feel like a lion or a king. I feel proud, like I'm in the clouds. I made that happen!

Women Who Love Female Ejaculation and Kunyaza

From Gogo, a market seller from Kigali, says:

> Kunyaza is very important because the man likes it. If a man can't do it then it is the woman's job to teach him. But if a woman cannot do it then she is dry, which is a problem.

Gogo's grandmother says:

> There are two types of men. Those that please the woman, and those that don't.

Marie-Josee, a 78-year-old Rwandan woman says:

> When I got married and my husband did it for the first time, it was an epiphany...He was very good at it, right until the day he died.

83-year-old farmer, Tatinne says:

> We have to sit together and decide who we will do that (kunyaza). This is important in a relationship. It's not about you ordering the other person what to do or using force or abusing a woman. I saw that when I was growing up but it doesn't happen anymore. Those are very old mentalities. If you want to move and progress you have to build together.

A Ugandan woman says:

> When my husband enters and my (vaginal) lips covers his penis. And when we practise kachabali, when the penis hits the lips, it will make me push out water.

A Rwandan sex therapist says:

> It all starts with the preliminary stage between husband and wife. Both need to be relaxed.
> It's not good to make love if she's dry, since neither will enjoy it. At first, she can teach you.

Ugandan woman says:

> Sex is sweet and enjoyable...it is the reason we are married...when there is no sex, there is no marriage.

A married Rwandan woman says:

> You feel like a real woman (when you ejaculate). I was afraid at first.
> It was like a dam breaking. I didn't know it existed. Kunyaza can
> strengthen a relationship. It's important. It really helps couples in
> Rwanda.

Kunyaza Sex Positions

Kunyaza is performed in different positions. What these positions have in common is that they allow the man to, almost without interruption, alternate from non-penetrative to penetrative stimulation and vice versa. Although penetration is not the most efficient way to bring a woman to climax, the combination of clitoral stimulation and slow thrusting during kunyaza sex will help bring a woman to erotic bliss.

Traditionally there are two types of kunyaza sex positions; traditional sex positions and modern sex positions. Traditional positions are the classical positions, which are the most commonly used positions for kunyaza stimulation. Modern positions are relatively easy to use for people in contemporary societies who are less athletic than their ancestors.

Kunyaza sex positions can be grouped into the following five; sitting positions, lying positions, positions from behind, standing positions, and positions during pregnancy. In all these sexual positions, it is important for the woman to be aroused before her male partner enters.

1. Sitting Positions

This classic sitting position of kunyaza is called *kwicaza*. It involves the woman sitting on the bent legs of the man, facing each other.

The modern sitting position of kunyaza involves the woman sitting on the edge of a bed with her legs widely spread apart. The man kneels in front of her in between her spread legs to perform kunyaza stimulation.

Another classic position is where a man sits on an area surface with his legs outstretched, as his female partner sits on top of him and wraps her legs around him. This position enables the man to be in full control to tease and penetrate the genitalia. As the man sits, the woman can straddle on top of him whilst he provides intense stimulation on her vulva.

2. Lying Positions

The modern lying position of kunyaza involves the woman lying on her back and the man sitting between her spread bent legs performing kunyaza.

The penetrating male partner stands in front of the woman whose legs dangle over the edge of a bed or some other platform like a table. With the receiving female partner's legs lifted towards the ceiling and resting against the penetrating male partner, this is sometimes called the butterfly position.

As the female receiving partner lies on their back, the male penetrating partner stands and lifts her pelvis for penetration or performing kunyaza. A variant of this position is for the woman to rest her legs on the man's shoulders, also known as the 'spread-eagle' position.

The coital alignment technique (CAT) lying position is a variant of the missionary position that offers clitoral stimulation during penetrative intercourse. The man starts in the missionary position with the woman's partner legs between the thrusting male partner. The man should enter and place himself quite high above the chest of the woman so that their pelvises are aligned. From there, the woman should lay her legs flat between the man and bring them together. The thrusting male partner should then shift his weight forward and back along with her body, keeping his hips close to the woman. Keeping his body flat against hers and rather than moving in and out, he moves up and down so that the base of his penis can stimulate the clitoris. The up and down motion will result in the man's pubic bone and penis base rubbing against the clitoris, increasing the chances to achieve climax.

3. Positions from Behind

The classic position from behind, commonly known as the 'doggy-style' position, where the woman is on her hands and knees and is entered from behind. Whilst the woman is on all fours she should lift her buttocks upwards and shake them to increase arousal. In addition, she can slowly twist her hips in a circular motion. This position is excellent for deep penetration and achieving a G-Spot orgasm.

Another variant of the position from behind involves the man kneeling on the bed with the woman in front as he stimulates and penetrates her from behind. She may hold onto her hips and / or torso.

Similar to the traditional doggy style position, but instead of being on all fours, the woman lowers herself onto her forearms while the man penetrates her from behind. The man can also lean forward and as his hands are free, he can caress her body and stimulate her genitalia at the same time.

4. Standing Positions

The traditional standing position involves the man standing and holding up the woman with one of his arms. This position requires upper body strength to hold the woman in one arm and perform kunyaza with the other arm / hand.

The first modern standing position involves the man and the woman standing face to face as he does kunyaza to stimulate her genitals until she is highly aroused before penetration. This position is relatively easy to perform if the woman is a similar height to the man.

Another modern standing position involves the man standing and the woman wrapping her legs around his waist while he supports her by holding her buttocks and back. For more support and deeper penetration, the woman can rest her back against a wall. This position does require a certain degree of strength and endurance from both the man and woman.

5. Positions with Pregnant Woman

The traditional pregnancy position of kunyaza involves the woman lying on her back on a bed and the man sitting between her bent and spread legs. On his knees, the man slowly teases her with kunyaza stimulation of her external and internal genitalia.

Similar to the classic missionary position, but with less pressure put on the abdomen or uterus. The woman lies on her back and raises her knees up towards her chest. The man kneels between her legs and enters from the front. A pillow can be placed under the woman's buttocks for added comfort.

The Best Sex Position For Kunyaza

According to Dr. Bizimana, kunyaza is best performed in one of the sitting positions. Bizimana advises that although it is better that the technique is performed whilst the couple are sitting, it can also be effective if the woman is sprawled on her back with the man kneeling between her legs.

Does Penis Size (or Shape) Matter?

It depends on the woman. Some women prefer a larger penis, others aren't so bothered as long as her male sexual partner has good technique and his penis is not "too small." What constitutes a "small penis" differs from woman to woman. Some studies show that the average erect penis is 5.5 to 6.5 inches in length and 4 inches in circumference. A micro (abnormally small) penis is 2.8 inches or shorter when erect, and a macrophallus (abnormally large penis) is 8 inches or longer when erect.

A national survey conducted by Moorgate Andrology, a UK penis enlargement clinic, found that most women prefer a penis at least 6.5 inches long with a "bigger than average girth" of at least 5 inches in circumference. The truth is for many women, size does matter in the bedroom!

Does Size Matter For Kunyaza?

For kunyaza, penis size doesn't really matter. Every man can use his manhood as an effective love instrument. Whether a man has an anaconda (large penis), banana-shaped, hook-shaped or 'pocket rocket' (small penis), he can provide a woman with ultimate pleasure by perfecting the kunyaza technique and having a good 'stroke game' during penetration.

What Are The Best Sex Positions for Different Penis Sizes?

The spread-eagle sex position is best for a small penis, the doggy-style position for a hook-shaped penis, the missionary position for a banana-shaped penis and a 'woman on top' position for a large penis.

Chapter 6: Female Ejaculation, Squirting and Kunyaza

"Don't block the water. Let it flow." – Vestine Dusabe, Rwandan sex educator

During sexual arousal and orgasm, some women emit a small amount of fluid from the urethra, and others emit a large amount of fluid. The process of the former is referred to as 'female ejaculation,' the latter is commonly referred to as 'squirting.' The topic of female ejaculation and squirting is a controversial one. Some Western researchers state that a woman's expelled 'squirting' fluid is urine, others state that it is female ejaculate. In contrast, many African sex researchers and sex educators believe that both the small and large expulsions of erotic fluid are female ejaculate. Presenting the controversial history of the female ejaculate, this chapter examines female ejaculation and squirting studies, investigates the G-Spot, and presents an illustrated guide on how women can ejaculate by way of kunyaza, oral and G-Spot stimulation.

What is Female Ejaculate?

Female ejaculate is a clear, watery liquid. It is not the same as vaginal lubrication or urine. Only a small and usually unnoticed amount of female ejaculate is creamy and white like male ejaculate. Female ejaculate is predominately prostatic fluid mixed with some glucose and may include trace amounts of urine (specifically uric acid, urea, and creatinine).

The taste and smell of female ejaculate may vary with a woman's menstrual cycle. At times it can taste and smell salty and somewhat strong, and at other times, fresh and distinctively light with an earthy aroma. Sometimes the ejaculate has no smell or taste at all, or it may have a faint smell and taste of urine.[39]

What is Female Ejaculation and Squirting?

Female ejaculation is the emission of fluid from the urethra (the tubular structure through which urine passes out of the body) during sexual arousal or orgasm. The expulsion of fluid is said to be produced by the Skene's

---

[39] Sundahl, D., *Female Ejaculation & The G-Spot*, p. 34

glands,[40] also referred to as the 'female prostate'. Some women report variable amounts of ejaculatory fluid ranging from 0.3ml to more than 150ml.

Although the prevalence of the female ejaculation phenomenon is difficult to evaluate, a 2014 French study estimated that 10% to 40% of women may experience regularly or sporadically an emission of fluid during orgasm. Another study estimated up to 54% of women ejaculate. Others report up to 90% of women in Rwanda can ejaculate.

During sexual stimulation, some women report the discharge of a large amount of fluid from the urethra, a phenomenon called 'squirting.' The noticeable secretion of female ejaculate is also referred to as 'cumming' and 'gushing.'

The Difference Between Female Ejaculation and Squirting
Whilst some people use the terms female ejaculation and squirting interchangeably, studies have found a difference between the two expelled liquids.

Squirting is said to refer to the large expulsion of fluid that excretes from the urethra during sexual arousal or orgasm. Whereas female ejaculation is said to refer to the small expulsion of fluid. Female ejaculation is sometimes referred to as 'true female ejaculation.'

Is Squirting the Same as Urine?
True female ejaculate is not urine but there is some debate as to whether large quantities of female ejaculate or squirting is in fact urine. Answering this question, sex researchers Barry Komisaruk, Beverly Whipple, Carlos Beyer-Flores and Sara Nasserzadeh said;

> Some people are under the impression that the secreted fluid is urine. It is not. The fluid resembles dilute fat-free milk and has a sweet taste. Although the volume may seem large during an orgasm, the total amount of liquid expelled rarely exceeds one teaspoonful (five millilitres).

---

[40] In female human anatomy, 'Skene's glands' or the 'Skene glands' are glands located on the anterior wall of the vagina, around the lower end of the urethra. They drain into the urethra and near the urethral opening and may be near or a part of the G-Spot. These glands are surrounded with tissue (which includes the part of the clitoris) that reaches up inside the vagina and swells with blood during sexual arousal.

Several researchers chemically analysed the fluid produced by female ejaculation and found that it contains high levels of glucose and an enzyme called prostatic acid phosphatase, and low levels of urea and creatinine. This chemical composition differs substantially from that of a woman's typical urine, which contains high levels of urea and creatinine and no prostatic acid phosphatase or glucose. A woman may experience ejaculation regularly, on rare occasion, or never.[41]

The History of Female Ejaculation

Published literature on female ejaculation dates back to more than two thousand years. However, scientific studies on women who ejaculate during sexual stimuli tends to be poorly investigated and is usually confined to a small sample of female participants. To date, both the nature and origin of female ejaculate remains controversial. Whilst modern day Western scientists and sex researchers continue to question the G-Spot (female prostate) – the reported source of female ejaculate and debate the nature of female ejaculation, many ancient cultures have historically acknowledged the female ejaculate.

From as early as fourth century China, the female erotic fluid was discussed by the ancient Taoists. In ancient China, Taoism has a 'three water' view of female ejaculation, which it linked the three types of female emission to corresponding levels of stimulation and arousal in women. In ancient Taoists texts, liquids excreted during arousal were believed to be imbued with mystical and healthful properties. Among the Taoists, delayed ejaculation is not a sexual problem but a desired outcome.

In ancient Greece and Rome, Aristotle was probably the first to write about female ejaculation, and the Greco-Roman physician and philosopher Galen is said to have known about it. Other philosophers such as Pythagoras, and Hippocrates pondered the nature of the female ejaculate. Galen gave the glowing tribute to female ejaculation in his treatise, *On the Usefulness of the Parts of the Body:*

This liquid not only stimulates the sexual act but also is able to give pleasure and moisten the passageway as it escapes. In manifestly flows from women as they experience the greatest pleasure in coitus,

---

[41] Komisaruk B., *et al., The Orgasm Answer Guide,* pp. 20-21

> when it is perceptibly shed upon the male pudendum; instead, such
> an outflow seems to give a certain pleasure even to eunuchs.

Amongst the ancient Indians, female sexual fluid was referred to as *amrita*, the 'nectar of the gods.' The spiritual tradition of Tantra which flourished in central and eastern India a thousand years ago, considered three distinct types of female emissions; the *suratham* (wine-like juice), the *sronithram* (blood-tinged emission), and the *suklam* (ejaculate). Tantric sex practitioners believed that sexual energy is an embodiment of divine energy, and that this energy can be intensified and carried through the body by conscious breathing, in preparation for full-body orgasms. Hindu Indians also gave birth to the classical text on the art of lovemaking, *Kama Sutra*. In the original text written by the religious sage Vatsyayana, female ejaculation was mentioned;

> The semen of women continues to fall from the beginning of the
> sexual union to its end, in the same way as that of the male.

During the 1600s and 1700s the Japanese erotic artistic movement tradition of *Shunga*, flourished where female ejaculate was considered an aphrodisiac. The prints depicted deeply intimate portrayals of erotic female fluid in such graphic detail that would even make many of today's modern 'sexually liberated' societies blush.

Even amongst the religious medieval Arabs, female ejaculate was discussed amongst conservative Muslims after the Prophet Muhammad affirmed its reality in the seventh century. Such discussions led to a new literary genre called *ilm al-bah* (erotology), dedicated to exploring the art of coitus and pleasure in ninth century Arabia. Erotology was the predecessor of sexology in the West. The nature and existence of female discharge during sexual activity was one of the most debated topics amongst the Muslim erotologists. The female ejaculation debate has continued in modern times as scientists analysed the biochemical nature and source of women's emitted erotic fluid, debated its existence, its source and attempted to explain the cause of the massive fluid emission during sexual stimulation.

Studies on Female Ejaculation and Squirting

Female ejaculation is elusive for most women and continues to be an area of mystery amongst researchers. In 1904, psychologist Havelock Ellis proposed that the female ejaculate was analogous to semen and originated from the Bartholin glands. Almost fifty years later, German gynaecologist Dr. Ernst Gräfenberg opposed this view by arguing that female ejaculation had little to do with lubrication. He came to this conclusion by observing women masturbate, noting that ejaculation occurred more frequently with palpation of an erogenous zone on the front wall of the vagina which later became known as the G-Spot.

It was Gräfenberg's contention that female ejaculation was secretion from intraurethral glands located underneath the G-Spot. Gräfenberg was adamant that the female ejaculate was not urine, which was the leading alternative hypothesis at the time. In 1982, American sex researchers undertook a chemical analysis of the female ejaculate. The study demonstrated a clear difference between the liquid excreted during orgasm and urine, a finding that was later confirmed by independent scientific studies. From these results, it was posited that female ejaculate originated from the Skene's glands, the equivalent of a female prostate.

An important study on the female prostate and female ejaculation was carried out by Dr Milan Zaviacic, professor of pathology and forensic medicine in Slovakia. Over twenty years Dr Zaviacic conducted extensive studies on the female prostate culminating in his monograph, *The Human Female Prostate* (1999). Zaviacic's research indicated that small amounts of ejaculate continually seep from the female prostate into the vagina. According to Zaviacic, the G-Spot is the female prostate and the female ejaculation is the prostatic fluid.

Following Zaviacic's findings, the G-Spot was recognised as a functioning female anatomical organ and was given the medical term 'female prostate' in 2001. Some people incorrectly refer to the female prostate as the Skene's glands. It has been postulated that the Skene's glands are the source of female ejaculation. This is because the Skene's glands and male prostate act similarly in terms of prostate specific antigen (PSA), which is an ejaculate protein. Some scientists use PSA as a marker to identify female ejaculate. Before the 'discovery' of the female prostate by Western researchers, it was thought that only men produced PSA.[42]

In 2003, Deborah Sundahl wrote *Female Ejaculation and the G-Spot*. A leading expert and pioneer in female ejaculation, Sundahl is an international

---

[42] Sundahl, D., 2014, *Female Ejaculation & The G-Spot,* p. 34

sex educator who specialises in teaching women and couples about this taboo topic. According to Sundahl all women can ejaculate as every woman has a prostate which produces female ejaculate.

Another significant study was carried out in 2007 by Austrian based urologists Florian T. Wimpissinger, Wolfgang Grin, Karl Stifter and Walter Stackl. Published in *The Journal of Sexual Medicine*, the researchers investigated the ultrasonographic, biochemical, and endoscopic features in two women who reported ejaculations during orgasm. Authors of *The Female Prostate Revisited: Perineal Ultrasound and Biochemical Studies of Female Ejaculate* paper concluded that the data of the two women presented underlined the concept of the female prostate both as an organ itself and as the source of female ejaculation.

The medical recognition ended the debate somewhat on the myth of the G-Spot (female prostate). However, debates concerning female ejaculation and squirting remain controversial as demonstrated in the following four studies.

Female Ejaculation vs. Coital Incontinence (Czech Study)

Fluid expulsion during female sexual arousal and its aetiology was studied in 2013 by Czech sexologist Zlatko Pastor. For this study, a total of 46 female ejaculation studies were evaluated including four reviews and five books. Pastor's paper, *Female Ejaculation vs. Coital Incontinence: A Systematic Review*, was published in *International Society for Sexual Medicine*. The study investigated female ejaculation (FE),[43] squirting (S),[44] coital incontinence (CI),[45] and vaginal lubrication[46] during sexual arousal and orgasm. The study aimed to clarify the causes of emitted fluid at ejaculation orgasm.[47]

The report concluded that female ejaculation orgasms manifests either as female ejaculation of a smaller quantity of whitish secretions from the female

---

[43] Female ejaculation is defined as an orgasmic expulsion of a smaller quantity of whitish fluid produced by the female prostate. Opinions regarding the quantity of expelled fluid vary from 1 ml to 30-50 ml.

[44] Squirting, or gushing, is defined as the orgasmic transurethral expulsion of a larger quantity of diluted chemically changed urine.

[45] Coital Incontinence (CI) is defined as the involuntary loss of urine in association of sexual intercourse. Urinary Incontinence (UI) is defined as the involuntary loss of urine.

[46] Vaginal lubrication is a plasma transudate which diffuses across the vaginal wall due to the activities of vasoactive intestinal peptide and neuropeptide Y. The composition and quantity of lubrication fluid change according to the intensity and length of sexual arousal.

[47] Ejaculation orgasm is defined as a physiological response occurring as expulsion of various quantities of fluids at orgasm that originate from the urinary bladder (squirting), the female prostate (female ejaculation), or a combination of both, and may occur at the height of sexual arousal.

prostate or a squirting of a larger amount of diluted and changed urine. Female ejaculation and squirting were found to be two different physiological components of female sexuality, and various studies report that 10% to 54 % of women experience the emission of fluid during sexual stimulation. The quantity of fluid ranging from 1ml up to 900 ml. Pastor's study noted that female ejaculation studies are very complicated to evaluate due to the various research methodologies and sample selections adopted to obtain data for such research studies.

The study reported that the source of female ejaculation is the female prostate, and the source of squirting fluid is the urinary bladder. Citing other research studies, Pastor states that women may expel various kinds of fluids during sexual activity. Vaginal lubrication is the most common physiological sign of sexual arousal, but some women may also eject varying quantities of fluid with different compositions from various sources at orgasm.

The study did note that further research is required to get a better understanding of the origins of the different fluids expressed during sexual stimulation. Below is a summary of fluids released during sexual activities based on origins and mechanisms according to the Czech study.

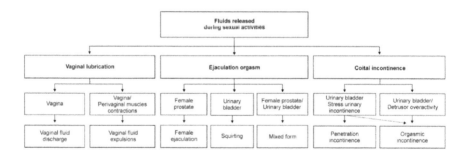

The Nature and Origin of Squirting (French Study)

The large expulsion of fluid from the urethra during sexual stimulation was investigated by a team of French researchers in a 2014 study published in *The Journal of Sexual Medicine*. The *'Nature and Origin of "Squirting" in Female Sexuality'* study conducted by Samuel Salama and his colleagues of Le Chesnay, France concluded that;

> squirting is essentially the involuntary emission of urine during sexual
> activity, although a marginal contribution of prostatic secretions to
> the emitted fluid often exists.

The researchers said that the large expulsion of (squirting) fluid is diluted urine, whereas the small expulsion of fluid is 'true' female ejaculation.

For the study, seven female participants, without gynaecologic abnormalities and who reported recurrent and massive 'squirting' fluid emission during sexual stimulation, underwent provoked sexual arousal. Aged between 19 and 52 years, the participants reported that they had their first experience of squirting during sexual stimulation within the past 5 years of the study. The squirting event was partner dependent, and in six of the seven women, this fluid emission was only possible during or after stimulation of the anterior vaginal wall, commonly known as the G-Spot.

Methodology
The seven participants were asked to urinate to empty their bladder, and a sample of urine was collected for analysis. This was the urinary sample before sexual stimulation (BSU). Immediately after, each participant underwent a ultrasonographic examination (US1) to confirm complete bladder emptiness.

Each participant was then left alone in the same examination room and started sexual stimulation by herself (with or without a sex toy) or with the help of her partner. As soon as the participant felt sufficiently aroused, a second scan ultrasonographic scan (US2) was performed to assess the size of the bladder. Left by herself again, each individual continued sexual stimulation until squirting occurred. The expelled fluid was collected into plastic bags. The squirting sample (S) was then analysed. Immediately after thus, a third ultrasonographic examination (US3) was performed as at US2.

The participants were asked to urinate again, and another sample of urine was collected for further analysis, urinary sample after squirting (ASU). All liquid samples (BSU, S, and ASU) were immediately frozen and stored for centralised analysis. Urea, creatinine, uric acid, and prostatic-specific antigen (PSA) concentrations were assessed in urinary samples before sexual stimulation (BSU) and after squirting (ASU), and squirting sample itself (S).

Results
All participants' US1 showed that participants' bladders had emptied. However, US2 (just before squirting) showed noticeable bladder filling, and US3 (just after squirting) showed that the bladder had been emptied again.

This suggested that female ejaculation, at least for these women, was largely urine. Biochemical analysis of BSU, S, and ASU showed comparable urea, creatinine, and uric acid concentrations in all participants. Yet, whereas prostate-specific androgen (PSA) was not detected in BSU in six out of seven participants, this antigen was present in S and ASU in five out of seven participants.

The ultrasonographic bladder monitoring and biochemical analyses indicate that squirting is essentially the involuntary emission of urine during sexual activity, although a marginal contribution of prostatic secretions to the emitted fluid often exists.

Biochemical analysis of the expelled fluid showed that this was definitely the case for two of the women in the study. The two women's fluid showed no difference between the chemicals present in their urine and the squirted fluid at orgasm. For the other five women, the analysis showed that the fluid was largely urine but it also contained PSA originating from the Skene's glands. PSA is an enzyme that was not detected in the women's initial urine sample. The presence of PSA in the emitted squirting fluid was ruled to be residue of 'true' female ejaculation. Based on the ultrasound scans data, scientists concluded that female ejaculation comes in two forms; 'true' female ejaculation and squirting.

Beverly Whipple, a neurophysiologist and female sexuality researcher, said that the term 'female ejaculation' should only really refer to the production of the small amount of milky white liquid at orgasm and not squirting. Speaking about the French study, Whipple says,

> This study shows the other two kinds of fluids that can be expelled from the female urethra – urine alone, and urine diluted with substances from the female prostate.

Neuroscientist and psychologist Barry Komisaruk adds,

> This study presents convincing evidence that squirting in women is chemically similar to urine, and also contains small amounts of PSA that is present in men's and women's true ejaculate. This study helps to reconcile the controversy over the fluids that many women report being released at orgasm. There are evidently two different fluids, with two different sources. Whether either of these fluids plays a physiological role – that is, whether they serve any adaptive function, is not known.

International Female Ejaculation Survey (Austrian Study)

An international online survey was carried out by Austrian urologists to study the characteristics of female ejaculation as perceived by healthy women. The study also found that fluid emission during sexual activity has a positive impact on women's and their partner's sexual lives. The women reported that fluid emission usually occurs during orgasm.

Methodology

The 2013 study carried out by Austrian urologists Florian Wimpissinger, Christopher Springer and Walter Stackl from the Department of Urology in Rudolfstiftung Hospital Vienna, found that most women who ejaculate do so on a regular basis and female ejaculation occurs in women of all ages.

320 adult women participated in the self-administered survey from April 2010 to October 2011. The female participants were from all over the world, from countries such as USA (35.3%), Germany (32.8%), Austria (9.4%), the UK (8.4%), Canada (5.0%) and Australia (2.8%). The survey consisted of 23 questions addressing the participants' characteristics, aspects of perceived female ejaculation, and its impact on women and their partner's sexual lives

The mean age of the participants was 34.1 years, ranging between 18 and 73 years. Their mean age at first ejaculation was 25.4 years. As regards to sexual orientation, 74.4% of women self-identified as heterosexual, 23.1% self-identified as bisexual and 8% self-identified as homosexual. As regards relationship status, 108 women (33.8%) were in a stable (unmarried) relationship, 90 were single (28.1%), 88 were married (27.5%) and 34 had a variety of sexual partners (10.6%). The study was the largest collection of data on the nature of perceived female ejaculation according to its authors.

Results

The study found that the volume of ejaculation was approximately 2oz for 29.1% of the surveyed women, and 83.1% reported that the emitted fluid is usually transparent like water. For 252 women (78.8%) their ability to ejaculate was an "enrichment of their sexual lives," 33 women (10.3%) were indifferent, 23 women (7.2%) "sometimes wished they would rather not ejaculate," and 2 women (0.6%) considered female ejaculation as a "pathological phenomenon."

Impact of ejaculation on participants' sexual life (n = 320)	n	%
Enrichment	252	78.8
Don't care	33	10.3
Sometimes I wished I would not ejaculate	23	7.2
I'd rather not ejaculate	10	3.1
Seen as pathological	2	0.6
	320	100.0

With regards to their partners' attitudes 288 women's partners (90.0%) regarded their ejaculation as a 'positive' phenomenon in their sexual lives, 16 women (5.0%) had partners who were 'indifferent,' and 2 partners (0.6%) had a 'negative' attitude. Whereas 14 women (4.4%) stated that their partners were unaware of the fact that they could ejaculate.

Partner's attitude towards female ejaculation (n = 320)	n	%
Positive	288	90.0
Does not know about it	14	4.4
Indifferent	16	5.0
Negative	2	0.6
	320	100.0

Various circumstances appear to trigger a woman's first ejaculation and her future disposition to ejaculate. 163 women (50.9%) could not cite any trigger for their first ejaculation whereas 75 women (23.4%) experienced their first ejaculation during sexual encounters with a new partner. Besides other triggers, the authors state that it may be assumed that the capability to ejaculate is linked with a new partnership, masturbation (4.4%) or even 'training for the ability to ejaculate' (3.1%) i.e. Tantra sex.

Regarding the source of female ejaculation; 141 women (44.1%) did not know where the fluid emissions during sexual arousal and orgasm came from, 54 women (16.9%) named the vagina as the source, and 51 women (15.9%) identified the anterior vaginal wall (G-Spot) as the source. The results indicate that the stimulation of a presumed G-Spot was not an exclusive trigger for ejaculation.

Perceived source of ejaculation (n = 320)	n	%
Unknown	141	44.1
Vaginal	54	16.9
Anterior vaginal wall ('G-spot')	51	15.9
External urethral meatus	48	15.0
Inner urethra	26	8.1
	320	100.0

The ability to 'let go' and experience an orgasm appears to be a very important factor, as are certain techniques of sexual stimulation for triggering ejaculation. 'Letting go' is the aspect of female ejaculation that is most difficult for women to master. It is also important for the woman's partner to reassure her more than once when she is in the throes of delight to let go and release.

Ejaculation was slightly more common during masturbation (53.4%) than during intercourse (48.1%). Interestingly, 62 women (19.4%) experienced ejaculation during anal stimulation. A further form of female ejaculation is spontaneous fluid emission (without sexual stimulation), which was reported by 33 women (10.4%); 13 of these experienced ejaculation during sleep. The authors report that this finding compares well with published data on sexual behaviour and the incidence of masturbation and orgasm among men and women during sleep.

Kunyaza Triggering Female Orgasm (Rwandan Study)
Rwandan sexologist Vestine Dusabe asserts that the large emission of fluid resulting from the kunyaza sexual practice is not urine. Rwandan sex researcher Dr. Nsekuye Bizimana's 2010 study, *Another way for lovemaking in Africa: Kunyaza, a traditional sexual technique for triggering female orgasm at heterosexual encounters*, concluded that the phenomenon of expelling large quantities of liquid during the practise of kunyaza is most probably female ejaculation, and unlikely to be urine except in some rare cases.

Methodology
Data collected from interviews and reader responses of kunyaza books was analysed to understand the nature of the fluid emission resulting from kunyaza sex. The participants, aged 70 years and above, were interviewed in 1986 by Dr. Bizimana.

99

Results

The interviews confirmed that most women reach orgasm with the kunyaza technique and that it is the main reason why it is practised according to the participants.

According to Dr. Bizimana, many women expel an abundant amount of 'water' during kunyaza sex from the moment the man penetrates the vagina with his penis. This may be due to biological reasons. Women who are not sexually experienced may initially think that there is something wrong with them Bizimana comments. Men in East and Central Africa prefer to have sex with female ejaculators. They are referred to as *kingindobo* or *shamirylikivu* in Rwanda, which respectively means "to put a bucket under her" and a "branch of Lake Kivu." These women are praised for their strong response to sexual stimulation.

Bizimana reports that there are several sources for the expulsion of large quantities of fluid. It can come from the Skene's glands, the periurethral glands, the Bartholin's glands and the sebaceous glands of the labia minora, which are directly stimulated during the kunyaza sexual practice. The vagina may also contribute to squirting fluid through a strong secretion of lubrication fluid. Though the liquid ejected during kunyaza is described as colourless to milky, sometimes of a thick consistency and with no particular odour.

The literal translation of *kunyaza* is derived from the verb *kunyara* which means 'to urinate.' However the expulsion which flows from kunyaza orgasm (KO) is not considered to be pure urine. This is because urine is called *inkari* in the Rwanda-Rundi language, whereas the secreted KO liquid is referred to as *amavangigo* or *ibinyare*. The different terms indicate that the liquid expulsion during KO is not urine but female ejaculation (or squirting), as the two liquids have differing properties.

The liquid expelled during KO is described as colourless to milky, thick consistency, with a strong odour. Urine on the other hand is usually yellow or brown in colour, generally water-like, and usually has a strong odour of ammonia. The quantity of expelled liquid during KO is reported to be up to three litres for some women. Rwandan men have a nickname for women who are prone to "pour rivers," *shami rynikivu*, meaning "put a bucket under

100

her." Women who have the ability to ejaculate are highly sought after in Rwanda.

Social scientists Marian Koster and Lisa Price of Wageningen University in the Netherlands said after studying sexual practices in Rwanda,

> The Rwandan women and men we interviewed were clear in their opinion that all Rwandan women are able to ejaculate, the ejaculation being different from the mere squirting of urine. Elongated labia are seen as crucial in this respect.

Disregarding Women's Testimonies

Some have pointed out that the controversy surrounding female ejaculation revolves around a reluctance to believe the testimonies of women who say they can ejaculate. Unlike the French and Czech studies, the Rwandan and Austrian studies affirmed the existence of female ejaculation from the female participants' testimonies. Rwandan researchers state that the large 'squirting' fluid emitted by women during the kunyaza sexual practice is not urine.

The real question is not whether female ejaculation exists, it is why many sex researchers and academics do not believe the testimonies of female ejaculators. Women should be trusted to report their own sexual experiences without judgement and the testimonies of female ejaculators should not be dismissed as unreliable evidence of its existence. The scepticism by Western academics about women's ability to report accurately on their sexual responses is a form of controlling female sexuality.

Women who ejaculate know that even if the fluid they emit during sexual arousal or orgasm comes from the bladder, it looks, smells and feels different from urine. Which is why many know that female ejaculate or squirting is not urine. The pleasurable experience of spontaneously expelling fluid in the height of orgasm is fundamentally different from the intentional act of urinating. American sex educator and writer Lux Alptraum says,

> in a world where women's narratives about their sexual experiences are routinely called into question, the debate over female ejaculation serves as a reminder that, when it comes to sex, we still don't believe women. Even when they're literally wetting the bedsheets with proof.

Can Every Woman Ejaculate and Squirt?

Almost all women have ejaculated, but not all are aware of it, according to author of *Female Ejaculation and the G-Spot*, Deborah Sundahl. "They mistake the fluid for urine or vaginal lubrication, and some may even believe they have urinary stress incontinence." Sundahl believes every woman is capable of ejaculation.

A study cited by sex researcher Beverly Whipple suggested that all women ejaculate during orgasm, but the volume of the ejaculate is often so small that it's undetected, remaining in the urethra or passing back into the urinary bladder.

Can Most Woman in Rwanda Really Ejaculate?
In Rwanda, it is believed that every woman is capable of ejaculation. British freelance journalist based in East Africa, Alice McCool, reported that the Rwandans she came across said it is rare to find a woman who could not emit large amounts of 'water' with kunyaza. Women who are unable to ejaculate are referred to as *rwasubutare* or *mukagatare*, both derogatory names in Kinyarwanda meaning 'granite splitter' and 'rock-woman' respectively.

Sexologist Vestine Dusabe estimates 80% to 90% of Rwandan women 'have the water' to ejaculate. She says.

> That water belongs to us. If we find it, it's wonderful!
> If not, it's a problem!

What matters is the man's ability to make it happen. Whilst pleasurable stimulation and woman's ability to relax plays a role in triggering female ejaculation, the man also plays a crucial role. According to Dusabe, the onus is on the man prepare the woman to relax her body and mind to produce water during kunyaza. East African men versed in kunyaza also take pride in meeting this expectation as kunyaza practitioner Ali Kakonge Simba says. A man who is not able to make a woman 'water' can lead to infidelity, "they'll cheat because they don't get to that point," he says. "That water disturbs them in their body."

Biological factors may also play a role in a woman's ability to ejaculate, urologist Florian Wimpissinger found from his research;

> We know of some tribes in Africa where all women are able to ejaculate.

Wimpissinger continues. "In my opinion, female ejaculation depends greatly on anatomical variation." Western sex researchers claim that certain sex positions and G-Spot stimulation increase the chances of a woman's ability to expel copious amounts of fluid. Certainly, some women are more capable than others of expelling large volumes of fluid. However, whether this is due genetic or biological factors is open to debate and is not conclusive.

Western Sex Educators on Whether Every Woman Can Ejaculate

Stella Harris, certified sex coach says:

> All bodies are different, so I don't think it's fair to say everyone can squirt. That just becomes one more way people can think they're broken or doing something wrong, and I don't think that's helpful. But I do think squirting is far more attainable than people realize [...] So many women are made to feel that they're 'gross'. This is why everything from the douche and fragrance industries to plastic surgeries for labiaplasty are thriving. So the idea that women would 'squirt' is difficult for a lot of people to deal with. It can be messy and in our culture it's often shamed by equating the fluid with urine.

Psychologist and author of *The Ultimate Guide to a Multi-Orgasmic Life*, Antonia Hall, says:

> It depends upon the woman and her body. We're not all wired to have huge gushing orgasms. But, in my experience, if a woman is open to learning how to ejaculate, she can do so rather quickly. Any expansion of pleasure takes an openness and connection with your own body. It could happen in a day, after a few attempts, or months of trying. Because all bodies are different, some women will be able to ejaculate and some will not. Either way, her willingness to explore her body and the pleasure that can be derived by it will create more intense and pleasurable experiences.

Tiffany Alyse Yelverton, sexual health expert, says:

> Articles by the scientific community contradict each other in regards to female ejaculation. It is not a myth and any woman is capable (of ejaculation). It requires continual stimulation of the G-Spot, which is also still debated. Because of the lack of knowledge of the female body, many people don't know where this is or how to stimulate it. It is also difficult for a woman to do herself with the hands based on the location, and also a difficult area to hit with a penis.

Alexis Thomas, sexual health educator, says:

> Everything is geared toward male desire in our society including the idea of female orgasms. Whenever we see the concept of female pleasure and orgasms in our society, it's usually an indication of a 'performance' that is catering to the male fantasy instead of a realistic idea of what a female orgasm looks like. All of this isn't to say that female ejaculation isn't something that is or isn't achievable. Instead of thinking of anything sexual as an achievement we should root ourselves in the idea of pleasure oriented instead of goal oriented. When we stress about this idea of squirting or not squirting it will totally make having a great orgasm difficult.

Deborah Sundahl, author of *Female Ejaculation and the G-Spot*, says;

> I ask women in my lecture to raise their hands—and I've done this for years so I have big anecdotal evidence—how many women stop in the middle of making love to go to the bathroom. And 30% will raise their hand. And then I ask how many of you wait until you're done making love, meaning, they have to pee during lovemaking, and they have to wait to go, and another 30% raise their hands. That's 60% of women holding back their ejaculate not knowing it's ejaculate, thinking it's pee...They hold back, clench their pelvic floor muscles. Some women don't even want to have sex because it feels funny... they think something is wrong with them when they have sex. This is a big, big, big problem, this is a big issue, and the correct information must get out there...Every woman who allows that to happen and brings it into their sexual life, and every man who has experienced it, absolutely loves it.

How to Increase Your Chances of Squirting?

An international survey of women who were capable of ejaculating found that four out of five reported that squirting enriches their love lives. According to Western studies, squirting generally results from a combination of G-Spot stimulation, relaxation and being in a comfortable emotional state. In addition African sex researchers recommend the following to increase a woman's chances of experiencing a gushing ejaculation;

- the kunyaza technique with prolonged clitoral stimulation,
- urinating prior to sexual activity,
- strengthening the pelvic floor muscles, and
- engaging in plenty of foreplay.

The G-Spot and Female Ejaculation

G-Spot stimulation is the most effective method to trigger female ejaculation according to several Western sex researchers. In contrast, East African researchers say that kunyaza is the most effective technique to trigger female ejaculation. Some women will find the stimulation of the G-Spot easier to experience the joys of ejaculation, others find the kunyaza practice to release the erotic fountain.

Where is the G-Spot?

The G-Spot is a sensitive area that can be felt through the front (anterior, belly-side) vaginal wall which is said to increase female pleasure. Located about half way between the level of the pubic bone and cervix (along the course of the urethra), the area was initially 'discovered' in 1950 by German gynaecologist Ernst Gräfenberg when he described the region and its potential in the *International Journal of Sexology*.

Gräfenberg's 'discovery' was largely ignored by academics and sexual health professionals until it was named after him by American sex researchers Dr. John Perry and Dr. Beverly Whipple. The Americans' ground-breaking book, *The G-Spot and Other Discoveries About Human Sexuality*, co-authored with Dr Alice Ladas was first published in 1982, and became an international bestseller. Other researchers such as Deborah Sundahl, author of *Female ejaculation and the G-Spot*, states that the G-Spot is the female prostate and its surrounding erectile tissue.[48]

Sexual health experts have been worried that media coverage of the G-Spot phenomenon would lead women to feel inadequate if they could not find the mysterious erotic zone. Italian researcher Professor Emmanuele Jannini said that women should not "hysterically look for the G-Spot," which he claims is not just a spot, "it's something much more complex." Using ultrasound to search for the G-Spot in his research, Jannini said,

> Something is there. We may call it a G-Spot or not – it doesn't matter.

---

[48] The erectile issue is the portion of the inner clitoris that surrounds the urethral canal.

Other researchers argued that the G-Spot is not a discrete anatomical entity.[49] It was suggested that the 'G-Spot' was not located in the anterior vaginal wall but is actually a combination of parts of the clitoris, urethra and vagina, which seemingly share the same blood supply and nerves. Dr. Helen O'Connell, a professional of urology, found that these three areas can stimulate each other during sexual play. Following a review of previous studies and her own research, the Australian urology expert, coined the term Clitoral, Urethral, Vagina (CUV) Complex to refer to the area commonly known as the G-Spot. O'Connell suggested instead of calling it a spot, it should be called the CUV Complex as the anatomically correct term given that the 'G-Spot' erogenous area is larger than researchers initially thought. Other researchers state that the G-Spot is the urethral sphincter, others state it is part of the clitoris, and some believe the G-Spot is a myth!

Is the G-Spot a Myth?

The attitude that the G-Spot does not exist still persists amongst some academics as demonstrated by an infamous study carried out by researchers in Kings College London. The British study investigated whether the self-reported G-Spot has an underlying genetic basis. Led by scientists at the Twin Research and Genetic Epidemiology Unit, published in 2010, the report claimed that there is no evidence for the existence of the G-Spot. It was suggested that the G-Spot may be a myth.

In what was the largest scientific study of the G-Spot, the study involved 1,804 female identical and non-identical twins, aged 22 to 83 years selected at random to complete a questionnaire on female sexuality and the presence or absence of a G-Spot. The study was the first to investigate whether there was an underlying genetic basis to the existence of the highly sensitive area on the anterior wall of the vagina, known as the G-Spot.

Even though 56% of the women reported to having a G-Spot, the researchers concluded that the G-Spot does not exist. They argued this based on the inconsistent pattern of the twins self-reporting a G-Spot.

The researchers expected that if the G-Spot did exist, both identical twins, who have the same genes, would report having one. In cases where one twin

---

[49] Hoaq, N., *et. al.,* 'The "G-Spot" Is Not a Structure Evident on Macroscopic Anatomic Dissection of the Vaginal Wall,' pp. 1524-1532

reported having a G-Spot, the researchers found that no pattern emerged of the other twin reporting it. Identical twins in the study were no more likely to report a G-Spot than non-identical twins, who only share half of their genes.

The researchers suggested that women's experience of the G-Spot is subjective and postulated that there is no physiological or physical basis for it.[50] Professor of genetic epidemiology and co-author of the research, Timothy Spector said,

> Women may argue that having a G-Spot is due to diet or exercise,
> but in fact it is virtually impossible to find real traits.

The study's lead researcher Andrea Burri said; "It is rather irresponsible to claim the existence of an entity that has never been proven and pressurise women - and men too."

Few weeks after the publication of the study, a group of French gynaecologists dismissed its findings in a conference held in Paris. "It is not a question of genetics but of use," said the organiser of the conference, Sylvain Mimoun. Leading French surgeon Pierre Foldes who pioneered a globally renowned technique to restore the clitorises to women who have been circumcised, said, the study's questionnaire started from the false premise that G-Spots are alike. He went on to say,

> The King's College study shows a lack of respect for what women
> say. The conclusions were completely erroneous because they were
> based solely on genetic observations. It is clear that in female
> sexuality there is a variability. It cannot be reduced to a yes or no or
> an on or off.

French gynaecologist Odile Buisson said the G-Spot was "a reality" and its effects could be observed in scans. To say otherwise, she added was "medical machismo." She called the study a "totalitarian" approach to female sexuality. Moreover, Mimoun said, the G-Spot will only be found by a woman who knows it is there and takes steps to cultivate it;

---

[50] Burri, A., Cherkas L., and Spector T., 'Genetic and environmental influences on self-reported G-spots in women: A twin study,' pp. 1842-1852.

In discovering the sensitive parts of her own body, the sensitive zone [G-Spot] will become more and more functional. But if she has never touched it and no one else has ever touched it, it won't exist for her as a consequence.

How to Make a Woman Ejaculate with Kunyaza

Betty Katana Nalongo, an experienced ssenga from the Baganda tribe in Uganda, teaches women how to achieve maximum pleasure. Using food props, the ssenga explains how a man should use his fingers and penis to provide clitoral stimulation to provoke a gushing from the woman's body, "A man has to rub here [clitoris], so that we can get an orgasm," she says.

Demonstrating to a woman how a man performs kachabali in the classic sitting position, Nalongo says,

> When we do kachabali we sit like this (woman's legs apart).
> And the man comes and sits here (in front of the woman).
> The man holds his penis like this (with his index finger and thumb).
> He puts his thumb here, and then he starts doing this (vertically tapping the penis on the clitoris)
> He can change his movements and do like this (horizontally tapping)
> Because when he does this and hits the bean (clitoris), then the (squirting) water comes.
> You have to do it while seated.

For Ali Kakonge Simba, there's nothing more exhilarating than the prospect of making a woman 'release water';

> When you are doing the kunyaza, you [should] brush the penis over the vagina, mostly on the clitoris. She will feel it nicely and she will start releasing water. That's what they call kunyaza. It is what women enjoy most. I also enjoy it. When I'm doing it. Because when I am with a woman who is dry, I feel pain

> It's the sound that comes out of the kunyaza style is what makes me and other men happy.

> When you see that water coming out you feel that you've done it, you feel that you are also a man.

On her radio programme, radio personality and Rwandan sexologist, Vestine Dusabe conversed with her female co-host Fanny, and a male caller about the wonders of a woman's water;

> Vestine: Have you ever seen that water?
> Caller: Yes
> Vestine: How did you feel the first time?
> Caller: I felt surprised.
> Vestine: How did you feel?
> Caller: It was very good...please tell the whites they should look for it as well!
> Vestine: Do you think white people can find that water?... Fanny, do you think white people can?
> Fanny: Well, they need to find the key first.
> Vestine: The key?
> Fanny: Yes, on the Eiffel Tower (clitoris). You put your finger on top of that. You touch gently and then water starts flowing. If a lot of water flows the town will be flooded. The water company can close down, we have all the water we need. It looks like Lake Kivu!

Western Sceptics of Kunyaza

Sex researcher Beverly Whipple and neuroscientist Barry Komisaruk state that they are not aware of any credible evidence that women can learn to control the process to enhance or decrease female ejaculation.[51] Many other Western sex researchers have reached similar conclusions due to inconsistence data on the female ejaculate, an apparent lack of trust in female ejaculator testimonies and a lack of information about effective techniques such as kunyaza that has a reputation of provoking female ejaculation.

According to many Western sexologists, G-Spot stimulation rather than the external clitoral stimulation, as practised with the kunyaza technique, is considered to be the most effective way to achieve female ejaculation. Rwandan sexologist Dusabe criticises Westerners' scepticism of kunyaza's effectiveness and informs Africans to not pay attention to the Western critics,

> White people do not believe in it because they don't know it.
> They have never tried to let the water spring.

---

[51] Komisaruk B., et al., The Orgasm Answer Guide, pp. 20-21

How to Make a Woman Ejaculate with G-Spot Stimulation

The fingers can give as much pleasure as the penis for some women. There are three basic motions to stimulate the G-Spot with fingers;

1. The first motion is the 'come hither' or 'come here' motion, where the index and middle finger are curled upwards inside the vagina and moved in and out towards the palm.

2. The second motion is called the 'windscreen wiper' motion which involves the curled fingers moving from side to side across the G-Spot to essentially wipe it.

3. The third motion is the use of the fingers to make a circular motion inside the vagina around the G-Spot area.

G-Spot stimulation is the preferred method to squirt for many women, as it is commonly believed that squirting is caused by stimulation of the female prostate (G-Spot). According to Kenyan sex therapist Maurice Matheka, manual stimulation of the G-Spot with the fingers is the most effective way to provoke ejaculation, as it can bend unlike the penis. Matheka cites the 'come here' motion as the best motion to stimulate the anterior vaginal wall where the G-Spot is located. Matheka says,

> The G-Spot is about an inch wide and you must stroke the area with either circular motions or with the 'come here finger motion'. It is important to ask her which motion stimulates her after stimulating an area for at least 30 seconds.

12 Steps to Make a Woman Ejaculate

Below are twelve easy to follow steps for men to make their women pour erotic waterfalls with kunyaza, oral and G-Spot stimulation.

1. Get comfortable - To begin with, your lady should lie on her back with her feet hanging off the bed. It is important that she is comfortable so that she can relax completely and not be distracted. You should sit or kneel in front of her and gently spread her legs to pamper her between her thighs with your penis.

2. Simple kunyaza – Firmly hold your erect penis with your index and middle finger and perform simple kunyaza on her by gently tapping on her lady parts. Rhythmically stroke the clitoris glans and labia minora with the tip of your penis. Make use of your other hand to gently caress and massage her breast, mons pubis or another erogenous zone to enhance pleasure. Take your time and do this for a few minutes.

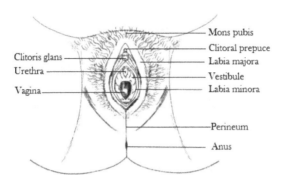

3. Find the G-Spot - Curve your first two fingers and slide them deeply into the vagina. Feel for a hard ridged or little soft spongy piece of skin behind the clitoris. This area is the G-Spot. You can massage it by making a 'come hither' motion with your curved fingers. Vary between fast and slow strokes, as well as gentle and firm pressure taps. Many men find it easier to locate the G-Spot when the woman is lying on her back. Some women may feel a need to urinate when the G-Spot is first stimulated, but if the stimulation continues the feeling will likely turn into a pleasurable feeling.

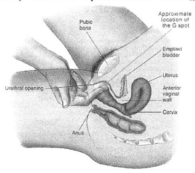

4. G-Spot stimulation – Keep the pressure firm and begin to make slow, circular movements with your lubricated fingers on the anterior vaginal wall area. Build erotic arousal by pressing firmly, or by tapping / stroking the area. If you're doing this right and she will soon be highly aroused. She may even release a sudden explosion of wetness.

5. Complex Kunyaza – This step involves the non-penetrative stimulation of the labia minora, vulval vestibule and clitoris with your erect penis. In horizontal and zigzagging movements, rub your penis on the vulva as shown below. Feel free to be creative as you playfully tease her lady parts with your manhood. The vulva may start to vibrate as she becomes more aroused. Continue to apply firm pressure. Applying pressure on the labia also indirectly stimulates parts of the K-Spot (inner clitoris).

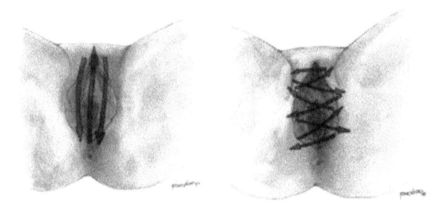

6. Follow her Lead – Pay close attention to her reactions to find out what non-penetrative stimulation motions her body prefers. Stimulate her preferred area and continue to do so until she becomes fully aroused and moist. Follow her instructions if she asks you to go faster or slower. Do not penetrate her even if she asks at this point, let the anticipation build. Gliding your penis along her moist labia should lead to pleasurable sensations all over her body.

7. Double Stimulation – Start the "overdrive technique" with your fingers and hand to simultaneously stimulate the clitoris and G-Spot

with your palm and fingers. The combination of the two erogenous zones will heighten her pleasure. Remember to take your time and be responsive to her as her body may shudder. The overdrive technique involves the following steps;

    a.   Use your first two fingers to stimulate the G-Spot area in the 'come here' motion.

    b.   Rest the palm of your hand on the clitoris glans.

    c.   Apply pressure on both the clitoris and G-Spot. Continue to simulate both erogenous areas.

8. Cunnilingus – Use your tongue to gently explore her clitoris and slowly feather her labia and genitalia with soft kisses and tongue play to increase arousal. Oral stimulation will provide a different but pleasurable sensation. Do not bite or be too aggressive. Reassure her with sweet compliments as you go down on her.

9. Don't Stop – As she comes close to ejaculating, she may experience a strong urge to urinate. If she tells you this, continue stimulating around the clitoris but with more rigour. The pace and intensity of the stimulation should gradually increase according to your lady's arousal.

10. Deep Thrusting – Your lady may start to expel some fluid, when she does, slightly open the labia minora with your fingers and slowly tap the inside with the penis. As you notice her becoming more aroused, begin penile-vaginal-penetration (PVP) with shallow / deep thrusts. Alternate the thrusting by making circle movements inside her vagina. Do not pound quickly and aggressively. Slow, long and deep penetrative thrusts is better to give her a more intense sensation.

11. Tease the Clitoris – After each deep thrust, remove your penis to rub and repeatedly tap the clitoris glans and labia minora with the shaft and tip of your penis to intensify arousal. The clitoris is likely to be extremely sensitive at this point. If you are feeling tired from the tapping, use your tongue to feather the clitoris instead. The small interruptions of penis withdrawal to tap her genitalia will help delay orgasm and prolong excitement.

12. Finish with Kunyaza – As your lady is about to ejaculate, let her lie on her back. Take hold of your penis and use the penis head to tap the clitoris, labia and vaginal opening (as shown below). To intensify the sensation, open her labia and use your erect penis to rapidly strike her lady parts until she can't take it anymore and her rivers start to flow.

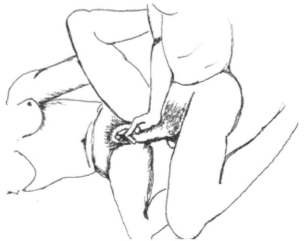

(Kunyaza - man stimulates woman's clitoris with penis head).

"If a man finds that water, it is a real honour." - Rwandan woman

"It's like water from a river. Trust me, it's a lot." - Rwandan man:

Chapter 7: Climax, Multiple Orgasms and Kunyaza

"Women orgasm within 5 minutes of kunyaza." – Dr. Nsekuye Bizimana, sex researcher

An effective technique for triggering female orgasm, the Rwandan sexual technique is said to bring more women to climax than penetrative intercourse. The kunyaza practice enables women to experience multiple orgasms, which is why it is preferred to intercourse for many African women. This chapter presents how women can achieve multiple orgasms, the effectiveness of kunyaza treating female orgasmic disorder, and how men can last longer in the bedroom.

Orgasm Statistics

Less than a third of women orgasm frequently by penetration. Most women achieve orgasm after at least 20 minutes of foreplay including clitoral stimulation. *Journal of Sex & Marital Therapy* took a poll of 1,000 women aged 18 to 94 years and found that most of them said that they could not climax without clitoral stimulation. According to a study cited by the late American tantra sex expert Psalm Isadora, one third of women have never experienced an orgasm. The other third of women rarely orgasm. And the final third of women have regular orgasms but a lot of them do not experience multiple orgasms.

A lack of sexual health education contributes to pleasure disparities in the bedroom. Studies have shown that while heterosexual men climax about 85% of the time during sex, heterosexual women climax just 63% of the time, research from the Kinsey Institute shows. The difference is known as the 'orgasm gap.'

Mutual sexual satisfaction can be elusive for couples, and therefore can cause a strain on a relationship. This often comes down to lack of communication and even sometimes a lack of education about one another's bodies and how they sexually function and achieve orgasm — especially when it comes to female pleasure.

14 Types of Female Orgasms

In the early 1900s, the founder of psychoanalysis Sigmund Freud argued that women can only have two types of orgasms - vaginal and clitoral. Freud believed that clitoral orgasms were a sign of sexual and psychological immaturity, and a mental illness. Later studies refuted Freud's claim and provided evidence suggesting that vaginal and clitoral orgasms are the same. Other studies concluded that all female orgasms are in fact clitoral orgasms. Some studies have found that women can have up to fourteen types of female orgasms. There is no consensus on this amongst sex researchers and the topic is still open to debate. Below is a summary of the fourteen types of female orgasms;

1. Vaginal Orgasm

This kind of female orgasm begins in the vagina and either stays focused in the pelvic and lower stomach areas, or spreads from there. The uterus, pelvic muscles, and even anus may begin to contract during vaginal orgasm. Those contractions are quite strong and may actually push out anything that was stimulating the vagina.

2. Clitoral Orgasm

Also known as vulval orgasms, the clitoral orgasm is the most common and easily achieved type of orgasm. This type of orgasm involve rhythmic contractions of the pelvic floor muscles, feels insatiable, and can be achieved without penetration. Most women need clitoral stimulation to climax. Also known as the K-Spot, the clitoris consists of the glans, legs, body and hood of the clitoris. According to some researchers the G-Spot is also part of the clitoral network, thus G-Spot orgasms are actually K-Spot orgasms.

3. Blended Orgasm

A blended orgasm is when both a clitoral and vaginal orgasm occur simultaneously. It involves both the involuntary contractions of the pelvic floor muscles that occur with the clitoral orgasm and the feelings of deeper physical and emotional satisfaction that occur with the vaginal orgasm. This kind of orgasm can happen when multiple areas of a woman's body are touched and pleasured simultaneously. Some women experience a blended orgasm when the clitoris and the G-Spot are stimulated at the same time.

4. G-Spot Orgasm

Also known as the 'Gräfenberg spot,' the G-Spot is located two to three inches inside the vagina. The G-Spot is a sensitive area felt through the anterior wall of the vagina about half wat between the level of the pubic bone

116

and the cervix. The G-Spot contains a large amount of pleasurable nerve endings and has a rough texture. The best way to have a G-Spot orgasm is to find the spongy area on the front wall of the vagina and apply pressure. G-Spot orgasms can be achieved by manual stimulation with the fingers in a 'come here' motion, or by the woman-on-top or rear-entry sex positions so that the penis will hit the anterior wall of the vagina.

5. Breast Orgasm

Some women are able to experience a breast orgasm or a nipple orgasm. It is said that arousing pleasure through the breasts and nipples awakens the chemicals responsible for love and bonding. According to a study reported in *Science of Relationships*, "researchers discovered that stimulation of the nipple activated an area of the brain known as the genital sensory cortex. This is the same brain region activated by stimulation of the clitoris, vagina, and cervix." Sex educator and kunyaza teacher Angelica Lindsey-Ali says,

> Some women can only reach orgasm when their clitoris is stimulated. For other women, penetration is necessary. I had a student who could reach orgasm through breast stimulation. Find out what makes you 'quiver.'

6. Kissing Orgasm

The kissing type of orgasm requires deep focus and some time commitment. The lips are packed with closely set nerve endings, classified as a mucocutaneous region of the body similar to the outer vulva, nipples, and clitoris. Basically, this means that they have the power to get you aroused. Slow lip synching, tongue rolling, and teasing are all part of building up your arousal and should, be a part of foreplay.

7. U-Spot Orgasm

The U-Spot has been described as a small patch of sensitive erectile tissue located just above and on either side of a woman's urethral opening. It may also include the opening of the urethra. The U-Spot orgasm can be triggered if the U-Spot region is gently stimulation, with the finger, tongue or tip of the penis. When stimulated, blood rushes to the erectile tissue that surrounds the opening, which can result in a strong erotic response accompanied with the large expulsion of fluid.

117

8. A-Spot Orgasm

The A-Spot orgasm is a deeply emotional and extremely satisfying event. These orgasms do not involve the rhythmic contractions of the pelvic floor muscles. A-Spot orgasms are also referred to as 'uterine' or 'anterior fornix orgasms.' The anterior fornix, posterior fornix and lateral (side) fornix are in the deepest portions of the vagina. Research has shown that pressure on this area stimulates the vagina to become lubricated. Women may be able to improve their natural lubrication by stimulating the anterior fornix area. The A-Spot is best stimulated when a woman is aroused, and her muscles are relaxed. Prolonged pressure on the A-Spot area, rather than repeated stimulation, is most effective to experience this type of orgasm.

9. Cervical Orgasm

The cervical orgasm is also known as the 'deep-spot orgasm' or the 'posterior fornix orgasm.' The cervical orgasm is one of the most intense orgasms a woman can experience by deep penetration. This type of can be experienced by stimulating the area located almost all the way back in the deepest part of the back wall of the vagina, just before the cervix. The cervix, located at the far (inner) end of the vagina, is the constricted opening to the uterus. When stroked by a finger, it feels somewhat rubbery, like the tip of a nose.

10. Mental Orgasm

A mental orgasm is also known as a mind, or fantasy orgasm. They can happen through the stimulation of the largest sex organ – the brain. This is what generally happens when you have an orgasm whilst sleeping. Some women can experience an orgasm from a conversation without any physical touch. Mental orgasms are brought on via intimate thoughts and exploratory fantasies nestled deep within the mind. Angelica Lindsey-Ali says, "The orgasm for a woman is mental."

11. Energy Orgasm

A full-body orgasm also known as an energy orgasm is an intense pleasurable experience that is felt all over the body. Full-body orgasms stems from the cervix and less from the genitalia. Energy orgasms can happen when a woman unlocks her sexual energy and allows it to flow freely on command. It can be achieved through a series of controlled breathing, a relaxed mind, deep meditation and kegel muscle clenching techniques. This type of orgasm releases the pleasure hormones (serotonin, dopamine and oxytocin) at will.

12. Zone Orgasm

Zone orgasms are ones that are experienced via stimulation of an area that isn't necessarily thought of as erotic. These are orgasms that are brought on by stimulation of that "special sweet spot." Areas such the clavicle, nape of the neck, inner thigh, or prostate can lead you to experience a zone orgasm.

13. Kunyaza Orgasm

Kunyaza orgasm (KO) refers to an orgasm induced by kunyaza after significant clitoral stimulation. The kunyaza orgasm (KO) is a combination of inducing female ejaculation and orgasm for a woman. When a woman induces a KO she experiences a heavenly bliss of joy and pleasure which results in the expulsion of 'water' and an euphoric state of climax at the same time. In order to achieve a KO, the man should continuously stimulate the clitoris with the kunyaza tapping and rubbing techniques until the woman's pelvic region feels like it is about to explode.

14. Multiple Orgasm

Multiple orgasms come in two forms: sequential (one right after the other, with rest time in between) and serial (one right after another). Unlike men, women do not experience a refractory period, where their brain is not responsive for some time to genital stimulation after an orgasm. This is not the case with women as their brains are sometimes more responsive after the first orgasm which is why women can have multiple orgasms in a row. The orgasms tend to be more prolonged and intense after the initial orgasm.

Multi-Orgasmic Women

During orgasm, activity peaks in the hypothalamus, an area of the brain that releases oxytocin, 'the love hormone.' After studying the brains of multi-orgasmic women, neuroscientists Barry Komisaruk and Nan Wise, found the activity of many brain regions during the second orgasm was significantly greater than the brain activity during the first orgasm. In other words, the second orgasm, in terms of brain activity, was more intense than the first orgasm. In contrast, when they studied the brain activity of single orgasmic women, they found that their brains deactivated after orgasm. Wise concluded,

119

I believe that the women who are easily orgasmic are more capable
of tuning into their sensations. And focusing on their sensations and
the experience is probably what empowers them to have more than
one orgasm. Multi-orgasmic women also release more oxytocin than
single orgasmic women.

How to Have Multiple Orgasms

Women are deeply erotic and naturally highly orgasmic. What prevents
women from experiencing multiple orgasms is often their mindset. When a
woman opens herself up, it is far easier for her to unleash her orgasmic
potential.

Reaching orgasm is one the peaks of the female sexual experience, but
surprisingly, this can be challenging for most women. Apparently one third
of women have never had an orgasm and even fewer have ever experienced
multiple orgasms.

Fortunately, women can learn how to overcome these challenges and learn
how to have multiple orgasms by tuning into their bodies, building up and
releasing sexual tensions to reach the blissful state of multiple orgasms. The
feminine sexual energy is truly powerful. Women are multi-orgasmic by
nature, but it takes some practise to unleash their orgasmic potential. Some
tips of how women can achieve multiple orgasms are summarised below;

1.   Let go and allow yourself to experience more pleasure! Focus
        on enjoying the moment and not the orgasmic goal. Do not
        pressure yourself into having multiple orgasms. Stay calm, relax
        and try not to force the situation.

2.   Pelvic floor exercises to strength vaginal muscles to have more
        control of the vaginal wall muscles.

3.   Breath control exercises to increase the amount of your sexual
        energy. Feel free to practise of the one the three breath control
        exercises developed by the late tantra sex educator Psalm
        Isadora, on a daily basis for a couple of minutes to feel more
        energised for sexual play.

a. Bliss Breath – Take long, deep inhales and exhales through your nose (don't breathe through your mouth), lightly constricting the back of your throat so that your breath makes a whispering sound.

b. Arousal Breath – Inhales and exhale rapidly through your nose as if you are hyperventilating. While doing this, pump your stomach back and forth in rhythm with your inhales and exhales. On the inhale, visualize that you are pushing a string forward from your navel and filling your stomach like a balloon. When you exhale, visualize pulling the string to the back of your navel to empty your stomach like deflating a balloon. This builds heat and arousal in your body.

c. Sound Breath – Stand up with your hands in fists and your arms overhead in the shape of a hockey goal. Take an inhale then pump your sides and exhale with a loud, strong breath that almost sounds like you're saying "huh!"

4. Engage in more foreplay by teasing yourself to the edge of the orgasm and then prolonging the climax. Allow sexual tension and anticipation to build up by not giving in when you feel the urge to release for the first orgasm. Stay disciplined and learn to control yourself.

5. Come close to an orgasm and then practise the breathing control exercise to relax and cool down in order for the sexual arousal tension to subside and build up again. Then do the deep breathing when you are about to climax and pull back again. This will help build up anticipation and sexual tension.

6. Stimulate another erogenous area (i.e. vaginal lips, breasts, clitoral shaft) apart from the clitoris after the first orgasm. The clitoris is often very sensitive after achieving climax. Once you have reached your first climax, continue to stimulate other erogenous zone to elicit another orgasm. For example, engage in G-Spot stimulation after achieving the initial orgasm via clitoral stimulation. You may need to give yourself some time to relax, recover and build up arousal again.

Six Steps to Bring a Woman to Climax with Kunyaza

Below are six easy to follow steps to bring a woman to climax within 5 minutes with the kunyaza practice. Each step should take between one to two minutes.

1. To begin with the man should playfully use his penis to; stroke up and down along the labia, tap the clitoris and make swirls around it whilst stimulating the clitoral hood.

2. The man should proceed to thump the head of the penis on the clitoris glans and rub his penis along the labia minora for increased pleasure.

3. After two minutes of stroking, tapping and rubbing of her genitalia, until she is fully lubricated, the man can then move his penis down to the entrance of the vagina and then tease her with some shallow thrusts, by going inside a little bit and then coming out.

4. Then he can continue to use his penis to swirl inside the vagina until she is close to reach the point of no return. The man should be patient and continue to tease her and have fun to build arousal.

5. The man along with the woman should explore what she desires more, whether shallow thrusts or deep thrusts or clitoral stimulation. Then he should proceed to do what gives her the most pleasure.

6. In order to heighten arousal, the man should continue her preferred stimulation arousal until she is ready to climax. It will make her orgasm easier and more intense. He should maintain firm pressure and tease her until the woman cannot take it anymore.

Kunyaza, A Treatment for Female Orgasmic Dysfunction

German-based Rwandan sex researcher and kunyaza expert, Dr. Nsekuye Bizimana, presented his research on the effectiveness of the kunyaza treatment for female orgasmic dysfunction at the 20th World Congress for Sexual Health (WAS) 2011 conference in Glasgow, Scotland. In his presentation entitled, *Kunyaza: An African contribution to the treatment of female orgasmic dysfunction*, Bizimana investigated whether the kunyaza technique used to bring women to orgasm in east-central Africa, could trigger orgasm in women from non-African countries suffering from orgasmic dysfunction. 55 women participated in the study conducted by Bizimana, who said;

> In this presentation, we again describe this little-known sexual technique, which has the reputation of strongly stimulating female orgasm and expulsion by the woman of large quantities of liquid during heterosexual encounters. We also report the experiences of the readers of our books and of those attending our lectures concerning female orgasms and expulsion of liquid by the woman during the practise of kunyaza and, in addition, the results of the chemical analysis of the ejected liquid.

What is Female Orgasmic Dysfunction?

Female orgasmic dysfunction refers to the difficulty or inability of a woman to reach orgasm during sexual stimulation. The male equivalent of the disorder is erectile dysfunction, premature ejaculation or delayed ejaculation. For women with female orgasmic disorder, orgasm is either absent or significantly reduced in intensity during almost all occasions of sexual activity. According to some sexual health professionals for a woman to have a diagnosis of female orgasmic disorder, significant distress must accompany symptoms and it must be present for a minimum of six months. It is also important to consider whether the difficulty with reaching orgasm is a result of inadequate sexual stimulation.

Reported prevalence rates for female orgasmic problems vary from 10% to 42%, depending on age, culture, duration and severity of symptoms. Only a proportion of women experiencing orgasmic difficulties, however, experience associated distress. Approximately 10% of women do not regularly experience orgasm, studies have found.

Method of Study and Results

The 55 heterosexual couples received instructions on the kunyaza practice and an anonymous semi-structured questionnaire in which the women were requested to respond to the questions regarding their orgasmic experiences.

There were three stages of the study to measure orgasm occurrence; one in which the man stimulated the woman's vulval area only during the sexual encounter, the second involved stimulating the vaginal area only, and the third stage involved stimulating both the vaginal and vulval areas during the sexual encounter. The vulval area was stimulated with the penis, using the kunyaza technique, the vaginal area was stimulated by way of penile-vaginal-penetration (PVP). The kunyaza technique consists of stimulating the vulval area of the female genitalia by striking it with the glans of the penis which the man takes in his hand.

The research found that from the 55 women suffering from female orgasmic dysfunction, aged between 20 and 56 years; 35 (63.6%) achieved orgasm by vulval stimulation, 15 (22.3%) achieved orgasm by vaginal stimulation, and 33 (60%) achieved orgasm by a combination of vulval and vaginal stimulation. The results also found that 20 (36.4%) did not achieve an orgasm, 11 (20%) climaxed once, and 24 (43.6%) climaxed multiple times during the sexual encounter.

Table 1 – Occurrence of orgasm with vulval, vaginal and vulval/vaginal stimulation

	No.	Age (years)			
		Minimum	Maximum	Mean	Standard deviation
No Orgasm	20	20	55	27.60	8.26
Single Orgasm	11	23	48	35.73	9.39
Multiple Orgasms	24	23	56	38.90	8.88

Figure 1 – Occurrence of orgasm with vulval, vaginal and vulval/vaginal stimulation

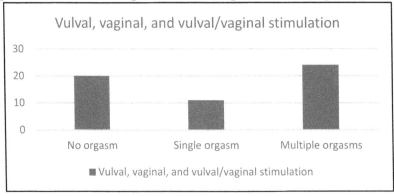

Results by vulval stimulation only

From the 55 women suffering from orgasmic disorder, 20 (36.4%) did not achieve an orgasm, 12 (20%) climaxed once, and 23 (41.8%) climaxed multiple times during the sexual encounter, in which only the vulval area was stimulated using the kunyaza technique.

Table 2 – Occurrence of orgasm with vulval stimulation

	No.	Age (years)			
		Minimum	Maximum	Mean	Standard deviation
No orgasm	20	20	55	27.60	9.63
Single orgasm	12	23	48	34.92	9.38
Multiple orgasms	23	23	56	38.61	8.69

Figure 2 – Occurrence of orgasm with vulval stimulation

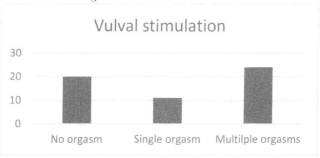

Results by vaginal stimulation only

From the 55 women suffering from orgasmic disorder, 40 (72.7%) did not achieve an orgasm, 3 (5.6%) climaxed once, and 12 (21.8%) climaxed multiple times during the sexual encounter, in which only the vaginal area was stimulated using the kunyaza technique.

Table 3 – Occurrence of orgasm with vaginal stimulation

	No.	Age (years)			
		Minimum	Maximum	Mean	Standard deviation
No orgasm	40	20	56	32.80	10.26
Single orgasm	3	30	48	40.33	9.29
Multiple orgasms	12	23	51	35.50	8.33

Figure 3 – Occurrence of orgasm with vaginal stimulation

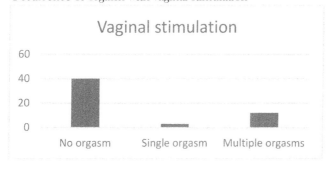

Results by vulval/vaginal stimulation

From the 55 women suffering from orgasmic disorder, 22 (40%) did not achieve an orgasm, 11 (20%) climaxed once, and 22 (40%) climaxed multiple times during the sexual encounter, in which both the vulval and vaginal areas were stimulated using a combination of the kunyaza technique and PVP.

Table 4 – Occurrence of orgasm with vulval/vaginal stimulation

| | No. | Age (years) | | | |
		Minimum	Maximum	Mean	Standard deviation
No orgasm	22	20	55	28.10	8.35
Single orgasm	11	23	48	35.36	9.29
Multiple orgasms	22	23	56	38.41	9.20

Figure 4 – Occurrence of orgasm with vulval/vaginal stimulation

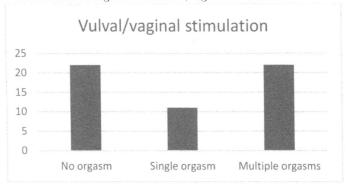

Conclusion

In conclusion, the study demonstrated the effectiveness of kunyaza in facilitating female orgasm, even amongst women suffering from orgasmic disorder.

Improving Male Performance with Kunyaza

The sexual discipline which is required by the man to effectively perform kunyaza can also help treat male erectile problems such as porn-induced erectile dysfunction (PIED) and premature ejaculation which can in turn prolong bedroom performance. For many African women kunyaza is highly effective in triggering female orgasm. In fact, a woman may reach orgasm within 5 minutes of kunyaza, often before the man climaxes, thus precluding the possibility of premature ejaculation. Many men suffer with shame and embarrassment feeling that they ejaculate too quickly, leading them to have anxiety about sex and their performance.

What is Erectile Dysfunction (ED)?

Erectile dysfunction, also known as impotence or ED, occurs when a man is unable to sustain an erection which is sufficient for sexual intercourse. The duration of time required to sustain a 'sufficient' erection varies from individual to individual. Some women require less penetration time than others to be satisfied. An erection normally occurs when blood flow increases into the penis, causing it to expand and become firm. Excessive amounts of pornography viewing can lead to ED studies have found.

What is Porn-Induced Erectile Dysfunction (PIED)?

Men with porn-induced erectile dysfunction (PIED) are unable to become sexually aroused with a partner, but have no such difficulties while watching porn, sex researchers have found. A 2016 study of 434 adult males linked extensive use of pornography to sexual dysfunction. The research, conducted in Europe, looked in-depth at online sexual activities and their effects on participants. The investigative team found that test subjects spent an average of three hours per week with online sexual activity. The most common activity was viewing porn, a behaviour engaged in by 99% of the study's participants. Heterosexual men with PIED found it difficult to be aroused in the presence of a female partner, but had no such difficulties while watching porn. Excessive viewing of pornographic material can also result in lower responsivity and an increased need for more extreme or 'kinky' material to become aroused.

Kunyaza Tradition Encourages Male Sexual Discipline

Men are encouraged to be sexually disciplined and avoid watching pornography, traditional African sex educators advise. Sexual abstinence prior marriage and self-restraint is deemed a mark of manhood in traditional East African cultures. In the Western world, many men's first exposure to sex is pornography, which teaches them that they should be forceful, demanding, and that if a woman says no, you just need to try harder to convince her. A woman's consent is not taught in porn and her pleasure is secondary to the consent of men. African sex educators encourage men and boys from a young age, the importance of self-control and having respect for women. Pornography is the antithesis of a healthy relationship, according to a number of sex researchers, as it could lead to arousal addiction, unrealistic attitudes about sex, body image issues, depression, sexual problems such as PIED and anxiety which can cause premature ejaculation.

What is Premature Ejaculation (PE)?

Premature ejaculation (PE) is uncontrolled ejaculation either before or shortly after sexual penetration. It happens with minimal sexual stimulation and before a man wishes to ejaculate. *The Diagnostic Statistical Manual of Mental Disorders* (DSM-5) classified premature (early) ejaculation as a sexual disorder. Premature (early) ejaculation is also defined when a man feels unable to control his orgasm, and climaxes in less than two minutes after vaginal penetration. PE is the most common male sexual problem, and it may have a profound negative impact on a man and his partner's love life. PE is said to affect up to 30% of men, and it may also result in unsatisfactory sex for both partners.[52]

How Long Do Men Last in Bed?

Various studies have been carried out regarding how long it takes for men to ejaculate during penetrative intercourse. Several studies have found that men often exaggerate their bedroom prowess.

Albert Kinsey's 1948 research found that 75% of American men ejaculated within the first two minutes of sex. *Journal of Sexual Medicine* published a study in 2005 that on average, intercourse lasts for 5.4 minutes. In a 2008 study in the *Journal of Sexual Medicine*, sex therapists said intercourse that lasted 1 to 2 minutes was 'too short,' 3 to 7 minutes was 'adequate,' 8 to 13 minutes was 'desirable,' and 14 to 30 minutes was 'too long.' A 2004 study in the *Journal of Sex Research* that included foreplay found that on average, people were indulging in 11 to 13 minutes of foreplay followed by 7 to 8 minutes of intercourse.

In another study, researchers conducted a 4-week study of premature ejaculation. Approximately 500 heterosexual couples participated in which where they were asked to document the duration of their sexual encounters using a timer and diary. The researchers asked the couples to start the timer as soon as vaginal penetration occurred, and stop the timer as soon as the

---

[52] Hsu, Y, et al., 'Treatment of premature ejaculation,' pp. 2-6

man ejaculated. The average (median) time before orgasm was about 6 minutes, which ranged from 6 seconds to 52 minutes. Circumcision and condom use had no significant impact in delaying or prolonging intercourse. The majority of men lasted between 4 to 11 minutes, with anyone lasting longer than 21 minutes being considered an outlier.

The study also highlighted men's tendency to overestimate their duration and performance in the bedroom. According to the researchers, the men's estimates averaged about 1.9 minutes longer than they really were—about a 31% overestimation over the 6-minute average.

A 2015 survey by sex toy retailer *Adam & Eve* revealed that on average, foreplay lasts 20 minutes, while the actual sexual penetration lasts 7.3 minutes. A British study found that the average sex session lasts 19 minutes, made up of 10 minutes of foreplay and 9 minutes of sexual intercourse.

How Long Should a Man Last in Bed?
It depends on the woman, her connection with the man and her mood. Some women would like a man to last at least 15 to 20 minutes, some say more than an hour, and some said it doesn't matter how long he lasts as long as enough it's for her to climax. There is no optimal time for all women. Open and honest communication is key to understanding what a woman's expectations are for how long a man should last in the bedroom.

What Causes Premature Ejaculation?
Most cases of PE do not have a clear cause. With sexual experience and age, men often learn to delay orgasm. PE may occur with a new partner. It may happen only in certain sexual situations or if it has been a long time since the last ejaculation. Psychological factors such as anxiety, guilt, or depression can also cause PE. In some cases, it may be related to a medical cause such as hormonal problems, injury, or a side effect of certain medicines.

How is Premature Ejaculation Treated?
In many cases PE gets better on its own over time. Treatment may not be needed. Psychotherapy and/or sex counselling is a popular choice of treatment for men with PE. Practicing relaxation techniques or using distraction methods can also help delay ejaculation. For some men, stopping or cutting down on the use of alcohol, tobacco, or illegal drugs may improve how well they can control

ejaculation. There are also a number of tried and tested sexual techniques like kunyaza which can help delay ejaculation and prolong bedroom performance for men. Some traditional African herbalists recommend traditional medicine to treat PE and improve sexual stamina.

The Kunyaza Treatment for Premature Ejaculation

The kunyaza technique can also help delay ejaculation by alternating between tapping the clitoris with the penis and deep penetrative thrusting. The kunyaza technique works well because it not only provides clitoral stimulation which many women require to climax, at both its tip and throughout the internal clitoral network, which includes the G-Spot.

Without ejaculation control, a man will not be able to truly satisfy a woman because he will come too early, come too late or be so focused on controlling himself that he will forget to be in the moment and respond to what his woman needs to he can provide her maximum pleasure. If the man feels like he is ready to climax, he should stop penetration and/or decrease the amount of clitoral stimulation with the head of the penis, as it is the most sensitive part. He could also perform cunnilingus (oral stimulation) or fingering (manual stimulation) to prevent himself from climax but at the same time continue to provide stimulation to the woman. It is important that the man trains himself to understand his body and how to delay his gratification to prolong the session for the woman.

The 'start-stop method' is a tried and tested method to learning ejaculatory control and lasting longer. A man should train himself to find when his ejaculatory inevitability occurs. This is the moment before orgasm when he is about to reach the point of no return. Instead of ejaculating, the man should refrain from stimulation and allow the feeling of orgasm to subside.

Alternatively, the 'squeeze' technique is useful. This is where the man is having intercourse and then when he feels like he is close to release, pulls out and squeezes the head of his penis where it joins the shaft thus producing a 'stop sensation,' helping him to be able to dull the sensation of wanting to orgasm. When he feels like that point of no return sensation has dulled he then re-inserts and starts intercourse again. Some men find squeezing their pubococcygeal (PC) muscles helps to prevent orgasm and delay ejaculation.

Satisfying Your Lady with Kunyaza

The male sexual ego is often linked to penis size. Whether a 'grower' or 'shower,' the obsession with having a large manhood plays on the minds of many men.[53] This has led many insecure men to undergo penis enlargement surgery or take non-surgical penis fillers to improve their self-esteem.[54] Men with low self-esteem tend to experience performance anxiety and have difficulties satisfying their female sexual partner.

Fortunately, the kunyaza technique does not require a large penis to sexually please a woman. It's about control, technique and patience, as some Rwandans advise in Olivier Jourdain's documentary, *Sacred Water*;

> You need to (psychologically) prepare the woman first and then you can even penetrate a little, maybe 5 – 10 times, before you begin.

> The most important thing is an erect penis, but you also need to have the knowledge!

> The woman should move her hips, then you start (kunyaza) brushing the clitoris with your penis.

> At one point she might tell you to put it in. But don't! Eventually you'll start to hear a 'pap,' 'pap,' 'pap,' sound...but you need to keep going until it's empty (from ejaculation). You must empty it!

> If you learn kunyaza, everything will be okay!

---

[53] A 'grower' is man with a relatively small flaccid penis that grows considerably when erect. A 'shower' is a man with a relatively large flaccid penis that doesn't grow much when erect.

[54] A 'penis filler' is a non-surgical procedure designed to increase the male sex organ's flaccid girth. The procedure involves the injection of a liquid, usually hyaluronic acid, into the soft tissue under the skin of the penis shaft. Online pornography has been blamed for the surge in men seeking penis fillers.

Conclusion: The Legacy of Pleasure

"We do not want our culture to disappear." - Vestine Dusabe, Rwandan sex educator

Sexuality in its various manifestations, is recognised as a fundamental aspect of being human. Considered a "basic human right," according to the World Health Organisation (WHO), everyone has "the right to pursue a satisfying, safe and pleasurable sexual life." However various cultures have different interpretations on how sexuality should be manifested. In most cultures there is little emphasis on women's entitlement to sexual pleasure. The belief that sex is or should be pleasurable for men is a universally held belief in many cultures. In contrast, the idea that sex should be pleasurable for women is not universally endorsed.

Only recently female pleasure has been a matter of interest in the West. This is due to the fact that more female professionals are entering the fields of sex therapy and human sexuality. Some researchers have referred to this as the "feminization of sex therapy." Despite this, there is a dearth of published literature on the specific ways in which culture and ethnicity define and shape female sexuality. To fill this void Dr. Cynthia Graham and Dr. Kathryn Hall wrote their pioneering book, *The Cultural Context of Sexual Pleasure and Problems.* An informative, thought-provoking volume of work on culture and sexual pleasure, the authors present the works of experts on the ways in which culture presents challenges to traditional sexual psychotherapist and sex educators. The work also challenges Western sexual educators to ponder their own unconscious biases and ignorance of alien cultures. The field of sexuality is by no means completely objective, researchers have their own inherent prejudices and subjectivities which may influence their interpretation of other peoples' sexual behaviour and attitudes.

As a British-born heterosexual male of Nigerian descent, I was cognizant of my limitations and inherent biases when carrying out the research for this book. I do not claim complete objectivity as I am well-aware that my gender and religious/cultural beliefs may have influenced the interpretations of the sexual behaviours and attitudes I came across during my research. In fact, being of black African descent was advantageous in some areas as I was able to extract some information from respondents quite easily because they felt an affinity towards me because of our "shared African ancestry." A couple of respondents initially expressed disapproval when they found out I lived in the "white man's land" of the UK. Trust was soon gained after I informed them that I was not part of a Western institution that wants to demean or disrespect their African culture. I was later welcomed as a "brother" and "given the secrets." At the same time, being a male independent researcher worked against me with some female respondents who felt uncomfortable speaking to me about intimate matters. I believe it is crucial for sex researchers and educators to be aware of one's own limitations and biases when studying other cultures, or teaching sex education.

Teaching Sex Education

The question of who imparts sex education and the framework in which it operates remains contentious. Some questions sex educators need to consider include; Who should teach sex education? Who controls the sex education narrative? What age should sex education begin? Should religion and cultural values be part of sex education? Should a sex educator teach content that is against their cultural and/or religious beliefs? Can a sex educator really be objective? Should the female orgasm be taught in sex education?

According to British-Nigerian sex and relationship blogger Dami Olonisakin, female orgasm should be part of sex education. "Young women should know that they matter when it comes to sexual pleasure and that sex is not just for men," says the UK-based sex blogger, also known as Oloni. Sex education is considered to be important because it supports young people to make informed choices regarding their sexual and reproductive health. It is also important for adults too, as many received poor sex education during their schooling. A reform of sex education is needed not only in the Western world, but in parts of Africa which have adopted a Western model of sex and sexuality education.

In May 2018, the Ugandan government launched the National Sexuality Education Framework 2018. It's Uganda's first ever guideline on sexuality education for young people in schools. Dutch academic Billie de Haas, believes the Framework is "problematic" because it's based on the country's religious and cultures values that instruct abstinence-only teaching. Uganda is a socially conservative country which believes in the virtue of premarital abstinence and marital faithfulness. However, de Haas believes Uganda should forego its social conservatism tradition for a liberal Western sex education model which teaches pre-marital sex, same-sex relationships and abortion are acceptable sexual practices. Whilst many in the West have supported calls to "liberate sexuality education in Africa," others have called it an example of "ideological colonialism." Pro-life campaigner and Nigeran author of *Target Africa*, Obianuju Ekeocha, argues that Western sex education "does not respect African cultural values and sexual mores." In addition, Rwandan sex educator, Vestine Dusabe, implores Africans to embrace their cultural heritage which teaches the importance of female sexual pleasure with the ssenga tradition.

Regarding female sexual pleasure in non-Westerners societies, Graham and Hall note that there is a lack of research in this area amongst academics. Much of what is known about sexual problems and their treatment comes from Western societies and Western-trained researchers, where scientific sex research and sexology were established. There is woefully little research examining effective methods of improving sexual pleasure and performance among non-white peoples outside of the West. Interestingly, little is known amongst Western sexual health professionals about kunyaza, Rwanda's sexual technique, that enhances female pleasure during heterosexual encounters. In traditional Rwandan culture, female sexual pleasure is as important if not more important than male sexual pleasure.

Cultural Impact of Kunyaza
The cultural impact of Rwanda's sexual practice extends beyond the small East African nation. Now practised in parts of the United States, Brazil and Germany, kunyaza is helping more women experience the joys of ejaculation. The ancient practice has also helped to change some modern-day attitudes and behaviours about women's sexuality. Female pleasure is a priority where kunyaza is commonly practised; men take pride in satisfying their female partner, and women regularly experience orgasms with their male partner. In Rwanda, up to 90% of women report ejaculation because of kunyaza, according to sex educator Vestine Dusabe. In the United States, sexual health

educator Angelica Lindsey-Ali said, 95% of her female students achieve ejaculation after learning about the East African technique. Lindsey-Ali says,

> Kunyaza has been extremely effective, even for women who thought they'd never be able to ejaculate. If I have taught the technique to 100 (female) students, roughly, I would say 95 of them are able to achieve female ejaculation by using kunyaza. This is of course, based on self-reporting.

Since learning about kunyaza in 1997, Lindsey-Ali furthered her research into the technique and traditional African-based sexuality. Now a specialist in kunyaza and African sexuality, Lindsey-Ali uses her expertise to eradicate the stigma of female ejaculation. The American-based sex educator is part of a growing number of female educators of African descent who are empowering women to reach their sensual potential. Speaking about her experiences teaching kunyaza, Lindsey-Ali says;

> The response to kunyaza has been overwhelming. People are a bit nervous to discuss it at first because some women believe that 'squirting' is something that women in porn do. But when I break down the history of it, it's rootedness in East African culture, and its centrality to the sexual experience of many couples, they turn.
>
> I think women are generally turned on by the idea of ejaculation but are confused by the mechanics of it. In the workshops/retreats, they have full access to ask questions and that allows them to be transparent and ask the questions they need to.
>
> My students love it! Kunyaza is, by far, the most requested technique that I teach. I even have some husbands who send their wives to me just to learn how to do it!

For kunyaza practitioners, it's the man's priority is pleasure the woman, and it's the woman's priority to enjoy being pleasured. Ultimately, the legacy of kunyaza is female pleasure. As one ssenga informed me;

> Women deserve pleasure, they have a God-given right to pleasure and men should know how to pleasure them with kunyaza!

Frequently Asked Questions on Female Ejaculation and Kunyaza

What is Female Ejaculation?

Female ejaculation is the emission of fluid from the urethra during sexual arousal or orgasm. The expulsion of fluid is said to be produced by the Skene's glands, also referred to as the female prostate (G-Spot). Some women report variable amounts of ejaculatory fluid varying from 0.3ml to more than 150ml. In Rwanda female ejaculate is called *kunyara*. In Tanzania and Zimbabwe, ejaculation is called *katerero* and *kutunda* respectively.

What is Kunyaza?

Kunyaza is a sexual technique originally from Rwanda, east-central Africa, which triggers female orgasm during heterosexual encounters. During the practice of this technique, with his penis in the hand the man stimulates the clitoris and other erogenous zones in the vulval and vaginal areas by rhythmically striking these with vertical, horizontal, circular or zigzagging movements. Stimulation often leads to *kunyara* (female ejaculation) and multiple orgasms in women. The kunyaza technique was first documented in 2005 by Dr. Nsekuye Bizimana in German. The first scientific study of kunyaza was published in 2010 for sexual health professionals.

What Does Female Ejaculate Look Like?

Female ejaculate can differ in appearance, texture and quantity. It can range from being a clear to a milky liquid, or from being watery to felling sticky. Amounts can range from a teaspoon, to a cup full.

What is Squirting?

Squirting is the large gush of fluid which expels from a woman's urethra usually caused by sexual stimulation.

Is Squirting the Same as Female Ejaculation?

Often used interchangeably with female ejaculation, squirting differs from 'true' female ejaculation.

How is Female Ejaculation Achieved?

Western gynaecological studies have shown that most female ejaculation occurs during stimulation of the G-Spot. As the G-Spot is stimulated, it swells and begins a fluid discharge through the urethra. In East Africa, clitoral stimulation by way of the kunyaza sexual practice is seen as the most effective method to achieve female ejaculation.

How Often Do Women Ejaculate?

Some women expel large quantities of fluid during sexual activity, others expel a little. Some women frequently experience orgasm, others rarely do so. Some women find it easy to ejaculate, others find it difficult. Most women and their partners perceive female ejaculation as an enrichment of their sexual lives. There are some women who consider female ejaculation to be shameful. Women are not a monolith. Some studies report between 10% to 54% of women can ejaculate during sexual stimulation. In Rwanda, researchers report up to 90% of women can ejaculate in some cases.

Why is Female Ejaculation Controversial?

Until recently, few published studies have existed about the phenomenon. There have been no conclusive scientific studies on female ejaculation. Much of the problem in arriving at a consensus relates to a failure to adopt generally agreed-on definitions or research methodology. Due to the ambiguous definitions, the variability of signs, and the subjective nature of obtaining data from respondents via questionnaires and focus groups, it is difficult to obtain objective data on female ejaculation.

What is the Source of Female Ejaculation?

Research studies note that the squirting fluid comes from one of the following four sources; vaginal hyper-lubrification, the Bartholin's gland, the Skene's gland, or the urethra.

What are the Two Types of Female Ejaculation?

Studies report the two types of female ejaculate; 'true' female ejaculate and squirting. Squirting is often referred to as 'springing' or 'water' in Rwanda.

Does the G-Spot Really Exist?

Yes it does for some women according to some studies. It is said to be located in the front anterior wall of the vagina.

Can I Teach Myself to Squirt?

Yes, it is possible for a woman to make herself squirt by clitoral and/or G-Spot stimulation using her fingers and / or a sex toy.

What is the K-Spot?

The K-Spot is the internal and external parts of the clitoris, which resembles the letter 'K.' The English word, clitoris is derived from the Ancient Greek word *kleitoris*. The kunyaza technique involves clitoral stimulation to heighten a woman's pleasure. Essentially, kunyaza involves using the head of the penis to stimulate the clitoris. Research have found that clitoral stimulation is extremely effective in bringing a woman to climax and ejaculation. Some studies suggest that the G-Spot is in fact part of the clitoral network, meaning the elusive G-Spot is part of the K-Spot!

Is Squirting the Same as Urination?

Some researchers state that squirting is urine, others state that it is diluted urine, and there are those who says it is not urine at all. In contrast, sex researchers in East Africa state that squirting fluid is not urine as it consists of different properties.

Does Kegel Exercises Help Women Squirt?

Yes, kegel exercises can help women squirt. The exercises strengthen the vaginal muscles which increases a woman's ability to squirt. The training of these muscles not only helps women ejaculate more easily, but more powerfully.

Why Can't Many Women Ejaculate or Squirt?

Female ejaculation is mainly psychological. Almost every woman is physically capable of squirting, but psychological barriers may prevent her from expelling fluid. Shame, guilt and sexual trauma also prevents many women from 'letting go' and experience the pleasure of squirting. 'Letting go' is the aspect of female ejaculation that is most difficult for women to master. It is important for the woman's partner to reassure her more than once when she is in the throes of delight to let go and release.

Why Do Women 'Hold Back' During Orgasms?

Many women 'hold back' before or during orgasms because they are worried of losing control or urinating. 'Holding back' is a sign that a woman is not fully comfortable and enjoying the moment with her partner. To really enjoy ejaculatory orgasms, it is crucial for women to 'let go' and not feel ashamed. That being said, she may need a trustworthy, non-judgement, and caring partner to help her feel at ease to let go.

Is Squirting a Sign of Orgasming?
No not all the time. Squirting does not necessarily always occur at the same time as an orgasm, and not every woman finds squirting pleasurable. When squirting coincides with an orgasm, it is referred to as 'squirting orgasm,' 'wet orgasm,' or 'female ejaculation orgasm.'

Should Women Feel Ashamed by Squirting?
There is absolutely no reason for a woman to feel squeamish or ashamed about squirting. Many women are blessed by God to expel large quantities of fluid during sexual stimulation.

Why is Female Ejaculation Banned in UK Pornography?
Pornography produced in the UK is censored through an amendment to the 2003 Communications Act. The ruling on "content that is not acceptable" by the British Board of Film Censors (BBFC) effectively bans female ejaculation from being depicted by British pornography producers. The measure appears to take aim at women's pleasure in which female ejaculation is deemed to be urine. Whilst the legislation may not necessarily prevent people from watching pornography, it does play into the notion that female ejaculate is obscene and shameful. The UK censorship undermines the legitimacy of women's sexual experiences.

How Many Times Can a Woman Squirt?
Women can squirt multiple times in one session depending on a number of factors. These are; the strength of her vaginal muscles, adequate hydration, sexual partner's competence, the physiology and psychology of the woman.

Why is the Female Orgasm More Difficult When a Man is Involved?
It is not uncommon for women to experience the pleasures of orgasm by themselves but are unable to climax with a male partner. Many women can climax with ease by masturbating but do not get to experience the joys of orgasm with a male partner. The most common reasons why women do not orgasm with their male partner are; male impatience, lack of trust, male incompetence, lack of communication between the two partners, an unwillingness of the woman to 'let go,' and incorrect sex education.

Do Women Enjoy Female Ejaculation?

Most women who experience ejaculation say that is feels pleasurable.

Is Kunyaza Effective for Men with Erectile Dysfunction?

Dr. Nsekuye Bizimana said, "Men suffering from mild erectile problems can still stimulate the woman's sexual organ. And also by virtue of tapping, the man's penis could stiffen and make penetration possible. I have come across several men who have also confirmed the effectiveness of this method."

Are Black People Naturally Good in Bed?

The history of sexual stereotyping towards black people and Africans dates back to when white Europeans first came into contact with the African continent. European travel books would describe black Africans as "animals" who would "fall upon their women, just as they come to hand, without any choice." Stereotypes about the sexual prowess of black people were equally presence in European literature, journalism, and art. The black hypersexual myth in Western popular culture continued during the transatlantic slave trade in which black men were perceived to have excessively high libidos, aggressively good in bed and possess exceptionally large penises. Black women also perceived to be hypersexual with an insatiable desire. As sexual partners, black people are seen as "naturally good" in bed by many non-black people in Europe, Asia and the Americas. This myth still exists today.

Why Is Black Culture Sexualised?

Black people and their cultures have historically been sexualised in the West due to Europeans' intimidation and misunderstanding of black / African bodies and cultures. For example, the *kizomba* sensual dance from Angola, southern Africa, has been misrepresented in many European and American circles. According to kizomba teachers from Angola, kizomba is "a very sensual but not sexual dance" but it is known in Europe as "the sexist dance ever." Similarly, the African term, *mandingo*, is commonly used in Western popular culture and pornography to refer to a hypersexual black man with an abnormally large endowment. Whereas in Africa, Mandingo people are a branch of the Mandinka people of West Africa. Predominately Muslims, notable Mandingos in history include Mansa Musa and Mansa Abubakari II. Today, some kunyaza teachers are concerned that Rwanda's sexual practice will be commodified and sexually exploited by non-Africans. Thus, it is important for black and African people to control their own narratives without fear of reprisal from others.

Bibliography

Book sources

Akande, Habeeb, 2015, *A Taste of Honey: Sexuality and Erotology in Islam*, Rabaah Publishers: London.

Akande, Habeeb, 2015, *Illuminating the Performance: African and Arab Erotology*, Rabaah Publishers: London.

Akande, Habeeb, 2016, *Illuminating the Blackness: Blacks and African Muslims in Brazil*, Rabaah Publishers: London.

Alordiah, Eve, *How to Squirt: An Expert's No-Sex Guide to Ejaculation for Women*, (e-book).

Bay, Roohallah, Ismail, Shaiful, Zahiruddin, Wan Mohd, and Arifin, Wan Nor, 'Effect of Combined Psycho-Physiological Stretching and Breathing Therapy on Sexual Satisfaction' in *BMC Urology*, March 2013, Volume 25, Number 13.

Baumeister, Roy F., 'Gender Differences in Erotic Plasticity: The Female Sex Drive as Socially Flexible and Responsive,' in *Psychological Bulletin*, May 2000, Volume 126, Number 3, pp. 347-374.

Bizimana, Nsekuye, 1989, *White Paradise Hell for Africa?*, Edition Humana: Berlin.

Bizimana, Nsekuye, 2009, *Kunyaza: Multiple Orgasmen und weibliche Ejakulation mit Afrikanischer Liebeskunst,* Hans-Nietsch-Verlag: Freiburg.

Bizimana, Nsekuye, 2010, 'Another Way for Lovemaking in Africa: Kunyaza, A Traditional Sexual Technique for Triggering Female Orgasm at Heterosexual encounters,' in *Sexologies*, Volume 19, Issue 3, July – September 2010, pp. 157–162.

Bjarke Oxlund, 'Let's Talk About Sex: Comparing Notes from Qualitative Research on Men, Relationships and Sex in South Africa and Rwanda' in Barrett, Barbara Ann, and Groes-Green, Christian (editors), 2011, *Studying Intimate Matters: Engaging Methodological Challenges in Studies on Gender, Sexuality and Reproductive Health in sub-Saharan Africa*, Fountain Publishers: Kampala.

Bridgeman, Bruce, and Roberts, Steven G., 'The 4-3-2 Method for Kegel Exercises,' in *American Journal Men's Health*, March 2010, Volume 4, Number 1, pp. 75-76.

Borg, Sonia, 2010, *Oral Sex She'll Never Forget: 50 Positions & Techniques That Will Make Her Orgasm Like She Never Has Before*, Quiver: Beverly.

Breitenbach, Maritza, 2012, *The Cookie Book: Celebrating the Art, Power and Mystery of Women's Sweetest Spot*, Hunter House Publishing: Berkeley.

Burri, Andrea Virginia, Cherkas, Lynn, and Spector, Timothy D., 'Genetic and Environmental Influences on Self-Reported G-Spots in Women: A Twin Study' in *The Journal of Sexual Medicine*, Volume 7, Issue 5, May 2010, pp. 1842–1852.

Chivers, Meredith L., 'A Brief Review and Discussion of Sex Differences in the Specificity of Sexual Arousal,' in *Sexual and Relationship Therapy*, November 2005, Volume 20, Number 4, pp. 377-390.

Comfort, Alex, 1993, *The Complete Joy of Sex*, The Chancellor Press: London.

Cormie Prue, Newton Robert, Taaffe, Dennis R., Spry, Nigel, Joseph, David, Akhil Hamid, Mohammed, Galvão, and Daniel A., 'Exercise Maintains Sexual Activity in Men Undergoing Androgen Suppression for Prostate Cancer: A Randomized Controlled Trial,' in *Prostate Cancer Prostatic Diseases*, June 2013, Volume 16, Number 2, pp. 170-175.

de Haas, Billie, Hutter, Inge, and Timmerman, Greetje, 'Young people's perceptions of relationships and sexual practices in the abstinence-only context of Uganda' in *Sexuality, Society and Learning*, Volume 17, Issue 5, pp. 529-543.

de Haas, Billie, and Hutter, Inge 'Teachers' conflicting cultural schemas of teaching comprehensive school-based sexuality education in Kampala Uganda,' in *Culture, Health & Sexuality*, May 2018.

Ekeocha, Obianuju, 2018, *Target Africa: Ideological Neo-Colonialism of the Twenty-First Century*, Ignatius Press: San Francisco.

El-Feki, Shereen, Mahon, Alyce, Mahon, Turner, Christopher, and Angel, Katherine, (editors) 2014, *The Institute of Sexology*, Wellcome Collection: London.

Ellwood-Clayton, Bella, 2012, *Sex Drive: In Pursuit of Female Desire*, Allen & Unwin: London.

Endsjo, Dag Oistein, 2011, *Sex and Religion: Teachings and Taboos in the History of World Faiths*, Reakton Books: London.

Frederick, David, A., St. John, H. Kate, Garcia, Justin R., Lloyd, Elisabeth A., 'Differences in Orgasm Frequency Among Gay, Lesbian,

Bisexual, and Heterosexual Men and Women in a U.S. National Sample,' in *Archives of Sexual Behavior*, January 2018, Volume 47, Issue 1.

Foxcroft, Louise, 2014, *Sexuality: All That Matters*, John Murray Learning: London.

Goldey Katherine L., van Anders Sari M., 'Sexual Arousal and Desire: Interrelations and Responses to Three Modalities of Sexual Stimuli,' in *The Journal of Sexual Medicine*, September 2012, Volume 9, Number 9.

Graham, Cynthia A., Mercer, Catherine H., Tanton, Clare, Jones, Kyle G., Johnson, Anne M., Wellings, Kaye, Mitchell Kirstin R., 'What Factors are Associated with Reporting Lacking Interest in Sex and How do these Vary by Gender? Findings from the Third British National Survey of Sexual Attitudes and Lifestyles' in *BMJ Open*, 2017, Volume 7, Issue 9.

Hamilton, Lisa, Fogle, Emily, and Meston Cindy, 'The Roles of Testosterone and Alpha-Amylase in Exercise-Induced Sexual Arousal in Women,' in *The Journal Sexual Medicine*, April 2008, Volume 5, Number 4, pp. 845-853.

Hall, Kathryn S.K., and Graham A., (editors), 2013, *The Cultural Context of Sexual Pleasure and Problems: Psychotherapy with Diverse Clients*, Routledge: London

Heiman, Julia R., and Lopiccolo, Joseph, 2014, *Becoming Orgasmic: A Sexual and Personal Growth Programme for Women*, Piatkus: London.

Hemmings, Jo, 2010, *How to Have Great Sex*, Vermilion: London. Hoaq, Nathan, Keast, Janet R., and O'Connell, H., 'The "G-Spot" Is Not a Structure Evident on Macroscopic Anatomic Dissection of the Vaginal Wall,' in *The Journal of Sexual Medicine*, December 2017, Volume 14, Issue 12, pp. 1524-1532.

Hsu, Yu-Chao, Hu and, Hsin-Chieh, and Huang, Shih-Tsung, 'Treatment of Premature Ejaculation,' in *Urological Science,* Volume 24, Issue 1, March 2013, pp. 2-6.

Jolly, Susie, Cornwall, Andrew, and Hawkins, Kate, (editors), 2013, *Women, Sexuality and the Political Power of Pleasure*, Zed Books: New York.

Kerner, Ian, 2004, *She Comes First: The Thinking Man's Guide to Pleasuring a Woman*, Souvenir Press: New York.

Kendrick, Keith, Haupt, Martin A., Hinton, Michael R., Broad, Kevin D., Skinner, John D., 'Sex Differences in the Influence of Mothers on the Sociosexual Preferences of their Offspring,' in *Hormones and Behavior*, September 2001, Volume 40, Number 2, pp. 322-338.

Komisaruk, Barry R., Whipple, Beverly, Nasserzadeh, Sara and Beyer-Flores, Carlos., 2010, *The Orgasm Answer Guide*, The John Hopkins University Press: Baltimore.

Koster, Marian and Price, Lisa Leimar, 'Rwandan Female Genital Modification: Elongation of the Labia minora and the Use of Local Botanical Species,' in *Culture, Health & Sexuality*, February 2008, Volume 10, Number 2.

Ladas, Alice Kahn, Whipple, Beverly and Perry, John D., 2005, The *G Spot: And Other Discoveries About Human Sexuality*, Holt Paperbacks: New York.

LaRousse, Jordan, and Sade, Samantha, 2011, *Clitology*, Quiver: Beverly.

Lloyd, Elisabeth, 2005, *The Case of The Female Orgasm: Bias in the Science of Evolution,* Harvard University Press: London.

Lorenz, Tierney A., Meston Cindy M. 'Acute Exercise Improves Physical Sexual Arousal in Women Taking Antidepressants,' in *Annals Behavioral Medicine*, June 2012, Volume 43, Number 3, pp. 352-361.

Maio Giuseppe, Saraeb S, Marchiori A., 'Physical Activity and PDE5 Inhibitors in the Treatment of Erectile Dysfunction: Results of a Randomized Controlled Study,' in *Journal of Sexual Medicine,* June 2010, Volume 7, Number 6, pp. 2201-2208.

Muhanguzi, Florence Kyoheirwe, '"Sex is Sweet": Women from Low-Income Contexts in Uganda Talk about Sexual Desire and Pleasure,' in *Reproductive Health Matter: Sexuality. Sexual Rights and Sexual Politics*, November 2015, Volume 23, Number 46.

Morley John E., 'Scientific Overview of Hormone Treatment Used for Rejuvenation,' in *Fertility and Sterility*, June 2013, Volume 99, Number 7, pp. 1807-1813.

Paget, Lou, 2011, *How to Give Her Absolute Pleasure: Totally explicit techniques every woman wants her man to know*, Piatkus: London.

Paget, Lou, 2012, *The Big O: How to have them, give them, and keep them coming*, Piatkus: London.

Pastor, Zlatko, 'Female Ejaculation Orgasm vs. Coital Incontinence: A Systematic Review' in *The Journal of Sexual Medicine*, July 2013, Volume 10, Issue 7, pp. 1682–1691.

Salama, Samuel, Boitrelle, Florence, Gauquelin, Amelie, Malagrida, Lydia, Thiounn, Nicolas, and Desvaux, 'Nature and Origin of "Squirting" in Female Sexuality,' in *The Journal of Sexual Medicine*, March 2015, Volume 12, Issue 3, pp. 661-666.

Salonia, Andrea, Fabbri, Fabio, Zanni, Giuseppe, Scavini, Marina, Fantini, Gemma, Briganti, Alberto, Naspro, Richard, Parazzini, Gori, Enzo, Rigatti, Patrizio, Montorsi, Fransesco, 'Chocolate and Women's Sexual Health: An Intriguing Correlation,' in *The Journal of Sexual Medicine*, May 2006, Volume 3, Issue 3, pp. 476-482.

Sun, Chyng, Bridges, Ana, Johnson, Jennifer A., Ezzell, Matthew B., 'Pornography and the Male Sexual Script: An Analysis Consumption and Sexual Relations' in *Archives of Sex Behavior*, May 2016, Volume 45, Issue 4, pp. 983-994

Sundahl, Deborah, 2014, *Female Ejaculation & The G-Spot*, Turner Publishing Company: Michigan.

Swift, Rachel, 1993, *How to Have an Orgasm as Often as You Want*, Da Capo Press: Philadelphia.

Sengendo, James, and Sekatawa, Emmanuel, 'A Cultural Approach to HIV/AIDS Prevention and Care: A Cultural Approach,' in *Methodological Handbooks, Special Series on Cultural Policies for Development Unit*, No. 1, 2001, UNESCO, Paris.

Skafte, Ina, and Silberschmidt, Margrethe, 'Female Gratification, Sexual Power and Safer Sex: Female Sexuality as an Empowering Resource Among Women in Rwanda,' in *Culture, Health & Sexuality, An International Journal for Research, Intervention and Care*, 2014, Volume 16, Issue 1.

Wimpissinger, Florian, Springer, Christopher and Stackl, Walter, 'International Online Survey: Female Ejaculation has a Positive Impact on Women's Impact and Their Partners' Sexual Lives' in *BJU International*, 25 January 2013, Volume 111, Issue 2.

Wimpissinger, Florian, Stifter, K, Grin, W., and Stackl, Walter, 'The Female Prostate Revisited: Perineal Ultrasound and Biochemical Studies of Female Ejaculate' in *The Journal of Sexual Medicine*, September 2007, Volume 4, Issue 5, pp. 1388-1393.

Wheat Ed., and Wheat, Gaye, 2006, *Intended for Pleasure: Sex Technique and Sexual Fulfillment in Christian Marriage*, Fleming H. Rivell: Michigan

Website sources

http://www.afrik-news.com/article14174.html

https://www.bbc.co.uk/news/stories-46073909

https://blog.mindvalley.com/how-to-achieve-multiple-orgasms/

http://uk.askmen.com/dating/love_tip/a-kunyara-primer.html

https://cosmopolitan.abril.com.br/amor-e-sexo/kunyaza-conheca-a-tecnica-de-masturbacao-a-dois/

https://www.cosmopolitan.de/kunyaza-so-kommst-du-mit-dem-neuen-sex-trend-zu-multiplen-orgasmen-nur-durch-klopfen-81263.html

https://www.cosmopolitan.com/uk/love-sex/sex/a17042937/non-penetrative-sex-ideas/

http://www.gabriellemoore.com/oral-sex-cunnilingus/kunyaza-or-the-african-secret-to-the-female-orgasm/

https://helloclue.com/articles/cycle-a-z/what-is-the-clitoris

https://www.lifesitenews.com/news/is-abortion-good-for-africa-try-asking-an-african

https://lovematters.co.ke/news/kunyaza-african-secret-female-orgasm

https://mauricetherapy.com/2012/11/08/how-to-make-her-squirt/

http://www.myblog.getrudemungai.com/getrude-mungai/

https://www.news24.com/Archives/City-Press/How-do-Africans-have-sex-20150429

https://newint.org/features/web-exclusive/2017/12/15/kunyaza-rwanda-sex-equality

https://www.newscientist.com/article/dn26772-female-ejaculation-comes-in-two-forms-scientists-find/

http://www.ozy.com/good-sht/rwandas-curious-obsession-with-explosive-female-orgasms/79053

https://www.psychologytoday.com/us/blog/all-about-sex/201610/childhood-sexual-abuse-how-men-can-help-women-recover

https://www.schoolofsquirt.com/make-her-squirt-easily/

https://www.standardmedia.co.ke/article/1144030166/getting-comfortable-with-sex

https://www.telegraph.co.uk/news/2018/06/25/almost-half-women-dissatisfied-sex-lives-55s-least-likely/

https://theculturetrip.com/north-america/usa/articles/can-all-women-squirt-female-ejaculation-pleasure-principle/

https://thisisafrica.me/sex-ed-bachelorette-parties/

Acknowledgements

"He who has not thanked people, has not thanked Allah."
- Prophet Muhammad

All praise is due to the one God, Allah. I praise Him, seek His help and ask for His forgiveness. I bear witness that Muhammad is His slave, prophet and final messenger. May Allah's peace and blessings be upon His messenger.

I am indebted to Dr. Nsekuye Bizimana for his published work on kunyaza and Rwandan culture. To Sara Salim, the patient, always helpful and knowledgeable who shepherded me throughout the long research and editing process of this book, I am forever grateful. To Azeez Akande, the advisor, I express my heartfelt thanks and appreciation. Special thanks to the ssengas, sexual health professionals, and academics (including Vestine Dusabe, Olivier Jourdain, Angelica Lindsey-Ali, Ali Kakonge Simba, Dr. Cynthia Graham and Layla Abdullah-Poulos) for their invaluable work. I am also grateful to the following organisations and academic journals; the *Society for the Scientific Study of Sexuality (SSSS)*, *Journal of Sex Research*, *International Journal of Sexual Health*, *Archives of Sexual Behavior* and the *Muslim Wellness Foundation*, for their work. To the people of Rwanda, Uganda and Kenya who provided me with a wonderful insight into their respective cultures, it's very much appreciated. To the reader, thank you for reading this book, hopefully it was somewhat interesting and beneficial.

Perhaps this book can help eradicate the stigma surrounding female ejaculation and help women experience the erotic joys of female pleasure. We should celebrate female pleasure, not question and regulate it.

"Leave a legacy" – Azeez Akande